Keeping Your Head Above Water

SALLY SHAVER DUBOIS

CONTENTS

	Acknowledgments	i
	Preface	iv
	Introduction	viii
1	Who Has Stress?	Pg 1
2	What Is Stress, Anyway?	Pg 10
3	Why Laughter?	Pg 18
4	Have You Played Today?	Pg 34
5	Exercise – Do I Really Have to Do That Today?	Pg 42
6	It's All About Your Attitude, Baby!	Pg 56
7	Giving Back	Pg 71
8	Relax, Reflect, And Recharge	Pg 81
9	Fishing for Food and Fueling Your Body	Pg 94
10	Stop Listening to The Music and Find the Lifeboats	Pg 112
	Endnotes	Pg 116
	Works Cited	Pg 119
	About the Author	Pg 130

ACKNOWLEDGMENTS

Wow! I really wrote a book, and my name is on the cover! For many years, the idea of writing a book was something I had thought about doing. However, I never got around to putting the words on the pages because I knew it would be a long process to organize my thoughts and ideas. Now that this book is complete, I want to thank those who helped me during the book writing journey and others who have inspired me to be the person God has created me to be.

Thank you first to God and the gifts He has given me to share with others during my blessed life. I am so grateful that He gave me a sense of humor which almost always assists me when those stressful trials come my way. I cannot imagine going through life without my faith as this world is full of shark-infested waters.

My husband Paul deserves a huge thank you for putting up with me and supporting my silly and creative antics. I love him dearly and appreciate his many gifts including his assistance in editing this book. My mother Kathy has always supported my creative endeavors. From the time I first set the table for and talked with my invisible clown friend at age three to all the many costumes she sewed for me over the years some of which I still utilize with my Silly Sally character, she has been in my corner. She drove me to music lessons, 4-H, girl scouts, church, and athletic practices which helped to shape me into the person I am today. She is the best Mom ever!

Although my Father, Chuck, died when I was only 20, his influence continues to shape my life. Thanks to my extended family for their support and humor over the years. My sister Mary was invaluable with Chapter 9. Her expertise in nutrition elevated the chapter. My brother Chuck assisted me as a beta reader. Thanks to my creative niece Andrea who utilized her talents to enhance the book cover! My special clown friends also deserve a big "thank you." Some of them are featured in this book while others were test readers and/or editors. My favorite and special teacher Ruth Mahon will always be an inspiration to me. In many ways, she is at the heart of my creativity.

A huge thank you to all the beta test readers who took the time to read and give feedback on this book. Their ideas and edits were invaluable to shaping the finished manuscript. Your time and talents were much appreciated! Debbi C. who went above and beyond utilizing her editing skills to shape the finished manuscript. Susan O. who was a test reader and lost her life just a few weeks after submitting her changes to me will forever be a part of this book. As an educator and friend, she had a zest for reading. She instilled the love of reading in her students. RIP my friend! Thank you to Angel Contreras who created beautiful illustrations that enhanced my words throughout the book! My photographer Destri Andorf of D & Orfs Photography took some great shots for the cover. Lastly, I want to especially thank Izolda Trakhtenberg who guided me through the book writing process and made many edit and formatting suggestions for the final version of the book. Her assistance was invaluable.

Illustration by Angel Contreras

PREFACE

The Flood

I woke up to the sound of water. As I stepped out of bed, the water reached my ankles in my basement bedroom. It had been raining for hours. A flash flood of water flowed under the walkout basement door from the nearby creek and inundated our ranch-style house. I stumbled out of the bed, grabbed my glasses and turned on the lights. Our house was quickly taking on water — 3 feet in all filling up the basement.

My dad had died a year earlier from a sudden heart attack, so it was just us three kids and my mom in my family home. When my dad died, I was 20 years old and experienced how life could change in an instant. One day, I was a carefree college sophomore, and the next day I was moving back home to assist my mother with the household responsibilities my dad left behind.

But on the night of the flash flood in 1984, I almost lost **my** life. I rushed upstairs as the rest of my family woke up. We realized our three golden retrievers were still in the back yard in their kennel and yelping for help. Their backyard kennel was next to this normally small-sized creek. I heard them crying out in the dark and knew they were trapped in the rising water. Their kennel had a top to keep them from jumping out, but now it prevented them from escaping to safety. I ran into the dark night and heard the water rush as the creek grew into a river of flood waters. Not realizing how dangerous the water had become in the pitch-black night, I ran straight for the dog kennel to free my furry friends. But as fast as I ran, I was swept off my feet even quicker. The fast-moving flood carried me downstream behind our neighbor's house. Fear swept over me as I bobbed along in the dark, dodging fences, a swimming pool, and trees with no life jacket. Did I mention that I am extremely near sighted and had taken off my glasses before running out of the house? Being nearsighted without my glasses or contacts, my fear of the unknown grew even greater with my limited vision!

In that moment, I knew I was in **big** trouble, and my life was out of my control. I cried out to God to help me as I tried to swim to safety. I believe God heard my cry, and my guardian angels threw me an invisible rope and guided me to safety. I found land and made my way back to the house. My family had no idea I'd left the house! God had saved me — even without a life jacket — miraculously, my head stayed above the water and I was not injured.

What happened to the dogs? We eventually saved them as well. Our kind-hearted next-door neighbor, an assistant football coach at our local university, played a huge role along with my brother Dave in the dogs' rescue.

With God's help, I survived that dangerous flood and literally kept my head above water on that summer night.

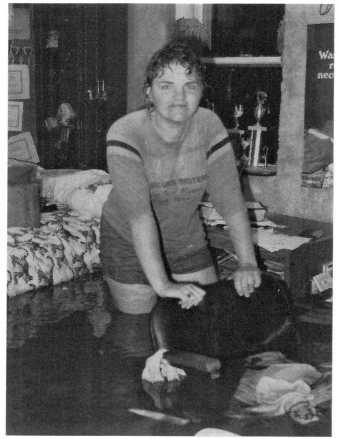

Sally in her flooded basement after she was carried down the flooded stream

You might not have been literally carried down flood waters like me, but you might be feeling like your boat is tipping over. Are you stressed out, overwhelmed, and full of anxiety or worry? Do you feel like you're struggling just to get through each day and keep your head above water with sharks looming nearby? Did COVID-19 pull you under without a life jacket?

Unless you have been living on a sandy beach somewhere with everything you could possibly want or need, have no issues with your family, have perfect health, and overflowing amounts of cash, you've certainly gone through periods of extreme stress in your life. Or you might be living with chronic stress right now and feel like you cannot possibly stay afloat. If this describes you, then this book can help! In the coming chapters, you will discover my L.E.A.R.N. principles to help you reduce stress and live a healthy active and joy-filled life!

-Sally Shaver DuBois

INTRODUCTION

As I was in the process of writing this book in 2020-2021, our world was hit with a once-in-a-lifetime pandemic event. Many of us never dreamed that life could take such a detour and cause so much stress, anxiety, and hardship for so many people across the world. In the United States, where I reside, we were simultaneously hit with political division, social unrest, and unprecedented weather events. There is no doubt that COVID-19 was incredibly stressful for many people, and I know that the coming years will bring more stressful situations for me and each person who reads this book.

I wrote this book to help you learn about the harmful effects of stress on your body and brain. I wanted to give you some realistic ways to prevent stress or cope when you feel like your boat has capsized in a shark-infested ocean of never-ending challenges. I find these ideas helpful. I share them with others because I know that chronic stress is one of the most common issues many adults and even children face.

Here's a little background information about me. I have worked in education for 30+ years teaching preschool-12th graders. I've been an adjunct instructor for college students and have provided teacher relicensure courses for educators.

In addition to my many teaching duties, I have coached many different sports, and I own a small business as a professional entertainer and speaker. Previously, I owned a personal training business. I utilized a converted school bus that I drove to childcare centers to provide fitness and creative movement activities for preschoolers. I have also worked many part-time jobs from mowing lawns, service industry jobs to taking care of animals.

Throughout my career, I have dealt with distress. My friends, who are nurses and physicians, explain the daily stress levels they endure. Regardless of your profession, you deal with stressful situations or stressful times of the year.

COVID-19 brought enormous work-related stress to many people. Healthcare workers and small business owners struggled to handle the mental and financial strain that the pandemic produced.

I don't have all the answers as none of us do. I have personally experienced stress during the pandemic, and in the past with relationship challenges, career trials, business failures, work stress, family worries, financial stress and many other life stressors. But as I move through life, I have developed some useful strategies to cope and can now even experience joy and peace when those stressful times come my way. Further, when I forget, other people in my life remind me of these principles when I capsize into stress-filled waters.

I found many of these ideas helpful as I navigated my way through COVID-19, and I'm hopeful that the principles I will share with you in the coming chapters will help you and get you back in the boat. Moreover, I believe they will guide you back to shore where you can live the life you were put on this earth to live!

I must acknowledge that I believe in God and have a strong Christian faith which helps to keep my stress under control and gives me everlasting hope. I believe that God is in control and try to yield myself to Him which makes the strategies that I will lay out much easier for me to accomplish. You may practice a different religion where you find peace and comfort or may not be religious at all. However, I hope you will still find techniques that you can use in these pages.

Are you fighting stress?
Photo credit: Destri Andorf (D & Orfs Photography)

1

WHO HAS STRESS?

So, who is stressed and why? According to the American Psychological Association (APA)[1] report **Stress in America**, 78 percent of Americans report experiencing at least one symptom of stress in the last month. This includes physical and emotional symptoms. According to the APA's report, the top four sources of stress are money, work, family responsibilities, and health concerns. The World Health Organization has reported that 80 percent of US workers noted stress in their jobs because of increased workload, interpersonal issues, lack of work-life balance, decreased job security, and poor job conditions.

COVID-19 certainly added more stress for many people. During the COVID-19 pandemic, the Centers for Disease Control (CDC) conducted a survey[2] and reported the pandemic was associated with several mental health challenges. The survey was conducted April through June of 2020. "Overall, 40.9 percent of 5,470 respondents who completed surveys during June reported an adverse mental or behavioral health condition, including those who reported symptoms of anxiety disorder or depressive disorder (30.9 percent), those with trauma and stress related disorders (TSRD) symptoms related to COVID-19 (26.3 percent), those who reported starting or increasing substance use to cope with stress or emotions related to COVID-19 (13.3 percent), and those who reported having seriously considered suicide in the preceding 30 days (10.7 percent)." I experienced stress during the pandemic and before COVID-19 at various points in my life.

To clarify, stress can be either enhancing or debilitating. It is about how a person reacts to certain experiences and events in life. The positive short-lived acute stress is called eustress and can be beneficial. We express it in our bodies as excitement, nervousness, or when we fulfill a meaningful challenge. Examples of eustress are when you feel nervous before getting up in front of people to make a presentation at work or when you experience excitement before participating in an athletic event. This type of stress stimulates the body for a short-term task and is a normal psychological response for most of us.

However, the type of stress I will focus on throughout this book is called distress which is a more severe and negative type of stress. Distress can trigger chronic health conditions. It can cause considerable psychological and physiological harm to the body and brain. This type of stress often results in chronic health issues when the stressor is experienced on a longer-term basis without stress management intervention.

This distress can either be from an external or internal stressor. External stressors are outside of our control such as unforeseen events, injury or illness, major life changes, the death of a loved one, or financial constraints. An internal stressor is likely self-induced. This may include our attitudes, perceptions, expectations, worries, fears, and lack of perceived control about our lives. See chapter 2 for more about the effects of stress.

Types of Distress

Financial Stress

As mentioned previously, many stressors can cause us distress. According to the APA's ***Stress in America Report***, financial concerns are one of the top reasons people feel stressed especially those making less than $50,000 per year. For those of us who have experienced financial issues with low paying jobs, loss of income, or mounting debt, this can be one of the most difficult things to deal with daily.

Many families were tremendously affected by job loss or furloughs during COVID-19. Personally, I lost most of my business income as an entertainer and speaker, and my husband Paul lost his job right before the shutdown. Fortunately, he eventually secured another job which was a huge godsend since my income will likely not improve for several years. We were also out of debt and had an emergency fund in place that kept us going until Paul found a job. We were not as stressed financially as many others during COVID-19 because we had planned ahead and worked on getting out of debt in the early years of our marriage. This was a huge blessing when a true emergency emerged.

In my opinion, financial stress can either keep you moving forward to financial freedom or take your anchor, with a loud thud, to the bottom of the deepest ocean. Monetary experts are far more adept with financial advice, and that is not the intention of this book. However, I will say that being free of massive debt can reduce anxiety in your life. When we suddenly lost income, a lack of huge debt comforted us and a kept our stress levels in check.

I encourage you to find a system and make financial choices that work for you and the people who live in your household. If you are constantly worried about how to make ends meet and living paycheck to paycheck or are living with massive debt, that is a huge stressor in your life. Seek help from a financial counselor. Read some financial help books. Change your spending habits. Take on a second job, if you can. You need to make a change, or the debt can sink your boat faster than just about anything else. While you are working through the financial stress, try some of the principles I will lay out for you in the coming chapters.

Work-related Stress

Work-related worry and tension are also a huge concern for many people. I guess that you might be reading this book because your career, current job, or lack thereof might be causing you strain and anxiety. You are not alone in feeling this way. According to the US Department of Labor, "The number-one reason people leave their jobs is because they do not feel appreciated."[3] When people are not acknowledged and appreciated in their jobs, they might experience stress or lose motivation. Therefore, productivity can suffer, and employees get frustrated and might leave. It is important for managers and supervisors to acknowledge and recognize their employees' contributions to their organization. However, you might not be getting this appreciation from your boss. Additionally, you might be experiencing stress on the job. If so, I have some ideas for you in the coming chapters.

One of my most hectic jobs was early in my teaching and coaching career. I landed a job in a small rural Iowa community with about 350 K-12 students. I was hired to teach K-12 physical education, high school health, 7th and 9th grade science, and was the high school girls head basketball coach. If you are familiar with teaching, you will note how many different preps were involved in this teaching assignment. For reference, I also lived in the small town of

500 people where the school district was located about "an hour from civilization."

As a younger single woman living by myself, there was very little to do in town except play tennis with some of my middle school students at the local park or visit Maude, an 80-year-old chain-smoking woman who befriended me and the single music teacher. If you have ever lived in a small community, you know the challenges of breaking into social networks or getting involved with the long-time residents, not to mention the lack of eligible single men who might be available for dates. You are considered an "outsider" if you were not born in the community. Basically, there was nothing to do in this small town outside of all the schoolwork and coaching I did.

In my early days of teaching, I did not handle stress well, especially when challenging situations arose. More times than I would like to acknowledge, I raised my voice at students or ended up in tears at the end of the day.

My dealings with parents added to the stress of the job. In a small town where the social life revolves around the school community, everyone believes they "own" the school staff. If you have ever seen the movie, Hoosiers, I was living it. Parents questioned my coaching abilities. A parent threatened to call the state department of education to revoke my teaching license. High school students left death threats on my voicemail, and many students challenged my authority.

One such stressful student interaction was when a high school boy purposely poured bleach into my 50-gallon fish aquarium in my science room because he was upset with something. Needless to say, the fish had it rougher than me that day, but my stress level skyrocketed. Another day, a student threw a roller skate across the high school gym when he was upset. When I confronted him, he told me to "F-off" which was resulted in a shouting match between us. In both situations, the school administrators gave me little support.

Last, at the end of my first year of coaching basketball with an 18-5 winning record, a group of parents tried to get me dismissed from my coaching duties. Thankfully, that didn't happen.

All these situations created tension and caused major burnout. I lasted two years in that job before I quit completely frustrated with the teaching profession. I headed to graduate school. In those early days of teaching and coaching, I was not highly effective at keeping my head above water when stress mounted.

Teaching can be an incredibly demanding career, and I hear educators express their high stress levels on a daily basis. According to a Gallop-Healthway Well-Being Index survey[4], teachers and nurses are at the top of the chart of experiencing a lot of daily stress. Physicians, sales professionals, and managers follow closely behind them.

During the COVID-19 outbreak, teachers experienced a huge amount of additional distress. Many of us barely kept our boats afloat as we navigated online, hybrid and in-person teaching all in the same school year. There were and are so many unknowns of how to teach while keeping children distanced, keeping masks on students, cleaning and disinfecting equipment, and navigating technology for virtual learners. Educators are still drowning as they try to keep up with the incredible amount of additional work and expectations. The school year 2020-21 was one of my most challenging and demanding times as an educator. I re-created all of my physical education curriculum to accommodate distancing students. I spent more time supervising students and disinfecting equipment. Most importantly, I was concerned about catching the virus and giving it to one of my family members. I felt like a brand-new teacher as I tried to navigate how to teach in this environment. I utilized many of the ideas in the coming chapters for myself, sometimes unsuccessfully, but I kept moving forward one day at a time.

Relationship Stress

Our relationships are another huge contributor to stress. Particularly, our relationship with our families can cause a great deal of stress. Although I have not been fortunate enough to be a parent, I have worked with children most of my life. I appreciate how much strain can occur as a parent or as a caregiver of children. When caring for, teaching, or parenting kids, they can stretch our patience into a frazzle in a hurry.

Being in a relationship with someone can also be a huge source of stress when we let it. Whether that person is a friend, child, spouse, significant other, family member, or acquaintance, interactions with other people can be some of the most stressful.

Many of us experienced increased strain during lockdown with family members day in and day out. How did you handle lockdown? I am guessing it was a challenge if you lived with others. On the other hand, if you live alone, you might have found it difficult not to have daily face-to-face contact with others. Lockdown stressed out many people.

Not being in a relationship can also cause worry and unhappiness, if we let it. Because I was single for over 25 years, I know the heartache of not having a significant other with whom to share life. I will say there was plenty of humor in the online dating and personal ads world which I will cover in chapter 3. I also found plenty of ways to be joyful as a single woman for many years. Having a life partner has been a blessing, but I was also productive and led a happy life when I was single.

I realize there are many other ways in which you might experience stress in your life. The first step is to acknowledge from where that stress is coming. Then you can begin to change how you deal with it. One of my favorite quotes which is attributed to many people including Henry Ford is,

"If you always do what you've always done; you'll always get what you've always gotten." In other words, if you want to lessen your stress, you must do something to change your ways or situation. If you hope to change what is happening in your life, you have to take the steps to do so because when nothing changes, nothing changes.

Stress is everywhere.

2

WHAT IS STRESS, ANYWAY?

Recently, I dreamed that I was a passenger on a bus with several other people. We traveled a familiar route near my childhood home. I had many suitcases and a can of paint and planned to exit, but I missed my stop. I told the driver I wanted to get off at the next stop as she smiled at me. When we reached the next stop a few blocks later, the driver stopped the bus for me. I began unloading my luggage down the steps onto the curb. I realized I needed a second trip onto the bus to retrieve the rest of my belongings. When I went back for more items and my can of paint, more passengers entered the bus behind me. I realized it was going to be difficult to exit the bus again. As I tried to get past everyone, the paint spilled and splattered on several of the other passengers. The driver started moving the bus down the road before I could get off.

"Stop the bus! Stop the bus!" I shouted, but the driver would not stop.

When I woke up in the midst of my screaming, I realized my dream revealed that I was on the stress bus because I was anxious and overwhelmed during that week. The luggage was the stress I carried around. The spilled paint spread my stress and anxiety to others. More people got on the bus because they were stressed and could not leave the stress bus.

What is causing you the most stress today? When we identify the causes of our anxiety, we take the first step in keeping our heads above water and rowing back toward shore. Then, we might be able to prevent those stressors or keep them from escalating.

Stress and Your Body

What does all this stress do to your body and brain? Stress in our lives can overwhelm us and suffuse our bodies and brains with psychological and physiological consequences. Stress was first mentioned in 1936 by Dr. Hans Selye.[5] He defined stress as, "The non-specific response to any demand for change." Another definition from the National Institute of Mental Health,[6] reads, "How the brain and body respond to any demand." A third definition that I find useful from Palmer & Cooper[7] says, "Stress occurs when pressure exceeds your perceived ability to cope." If we perceive something as worrying, our bodies will be stressed even if someone else does not become anxious in the same situation.

The systems of the body continually try to keep us in a stable equilibrium or state of internal balance. This state is called homeostasis. In acute or short-term stress, the body reacts with the "fight or flight" response. Fight or flight was first studied and researched by Walter Bradford Cannon in 1915.[8] This response is a good thing in emergencies when our sympathetic adrenal system engages and changes with the release of hormones. These secreted stress hormones boost our energy to get out of danger or perform a heroic task in an emergency. An example of this might be when a person lifts a heavy object or carries someone to safety during a crisis.

Specifically, our bodies release the stress hormones adrenalin and cortisol when we are anxious. This increases blood pressure, blood sugar, and can suppress the immune system. A series of other physiological responses follow. These include decreased blood flow to major muscle groups, increased heart rate, digestive issues, and constriction of blood vessels. They can even temporarily affect our vision and hearing.

Usually, after the perceived threat has passed, our bodies recover and return to the non-stressed homeostasis state. However, if our bodies are in constant flight or fight response from being overly stressed, or we have experienced trauma and have not dealt with it, long-term health issues can occur. These issues might be heart disease, weight gain, especially belly fat, anxiety, depression and disrupted sleep. If we do not learn how to manage our distress effectively, long-term health consequences are almost certain.

Measuring Stress Levels

Anxiety levels may be a challenge to measure as often stress is a subjective perception of what is traumatic to each person. One tool that might be helpful in determining stress levels is The Perceived Stress Scale (PSS) first utilized in a 1983 study.[9] "The PSS can be used to determine whether 'appraised' stress is an etiological or risk factor in behavioral disorders or disease." This tool can help examine the role that stress levels play in disease and behavioral disorders.

Another way to measure the stress is to complete the life-events scale. These inventories ask respondents to numerically rank how they feel about a variety of current life events such as socializing, money, family situations and health issues. Although it is difficult to statistically quantify stress in your life, you probably feel the effects of strain when it occurs.

Several things cause me perceived psychological stress. Like many people, I am afraid of heights and even have a hard time peering over a balcony. When I am up high, my brain perceives the situation as worrisome and responds physiologically. My blood pressure rises and pulse rate increases. I believe this fear of heights began when I was a child when one of my brothers coerced me into riding my bicycle down a steep incline. I was never hurt badly when I rode down the huge "devil's hill" in our neighborhood, but my perception was altered when he gave me a gentle shove before I was ready to venture down on my own. This experience, along with other stressful experiences being up high, began my discomfort with being in high places. Now, when I do activities, such as riding on a ski lift, jumping off a diving board, or driving a car on a road with impressive drop-offs, I am uncomfortable and worried even though the people who are with me might be having a wonderful and relaxing time. When possible, I avoid high places but can tolerate them especially if I know my reward will be to ski down a mountain slope. I try not to let my perception of the stressor take over and cause me unhealthy anxiety. Moreover, I refuse to let it keep me from pursuing the fun that might occur after being in a high place.

How Do You Deal With Stress?

As I discussed in the last chapter, we all have situations in our lives that cause us much tension beyond the psychological stressors. At times, we might deal with stress in healthy ways that work for us. We might take a walk, work on a hobby, or talk to a friend. But at other times, we might do unhealthy things to deal with anxiety. We might drink too much alcohol, smoke, shop, spend too much time surfing the internet, play video games, check out emotionally, or eat too much junk food. If you find yourself doing these unhealthy things more often than working through your stressors in healthy ways and your life becomes unmanageable, you can get help. You might try to find out more about addiction in a

12-step group. Further, please consider talking with a counselor or clergy at a church.

I admit that if I am not careful to follow my own principles, I might eat unhealthy foods, worry about things, or surf on social media sites to help me relieve distress in my life. I am not advocating that checking our social media accounts within reason, having concerns about our challenges, having an adult beverage or eating some chips once in a while is wrong. Rather, it's when we do these things in excess to avoid dealing with stress that is unhealthy. If you haven't found ways to deal with your anxiety, you likely risk many physical issues and other long-term health issues.

Think about things that might cause you perceived distress and how you react. Do you let these situations or things prevent you from getting out of the water and back into the boat? How do you react when you have had a stressful day or encounter stress over a period of time? Do you make unhealthy choices because of the way you are coping with anxiety?

Years ago, my young niece Andrea responded in the only way a preschooler could when her dad came home from a stressful day and announced that he had experienced a "hair on fire day." He often uses this statement when he has had a difficult and stressful day. Little Andrea immediately asked her dad if he had stopped, dropped, and rolled. Children are very literal at times, but this suggestion did have value beyond the laugh it gave my family.

Perhaps if my brother had stopped what he was doing to take a deep breath and get away from the stressor that was causing his "hair on fire" day, he could have eased the tension. He might have dropped what he was doing and realized how he was responding to the stress. Then, he could have tried an intervention such as deep breathing or taking a walk. Or, he could have just rolled with the "fire" with humor, prayer, or finding someone to help deal with the situation. All of these ideas would have been ways my brother could have managed his stressful day. We all experience those "hair on fire" days. Thus, we need to develop useful stress management techniques to ensure we can manage the acute stress before it becomes a chronic stress situation.

Stress and Resilience

A study at the Mayo Clinic[10] evaluated the association of resilience with lower stress and improved mental health with nearly 2,000 corporate executives and business professionals. The study concluded that those participants who exhibited higher resilience in the workplace environment were associated with "better mental health, reduced stress, and greater well-being. An increasingly recognized protective factor against stress is resilience. Resilience is defined as one's ability to bounce back from adversity and view adversity as an opportunity for growth." This study makes a lot of sense when you consider people who have endured significant stress and hardship in their lives yet lived well into their senior years. Those individuals likely were resilient and able to cope with stress more effectively.

Consider Louis Zamperini who was featured in the book and movie, **Unbroken**[11]. He was an Olympic runner in the 1936 Olympics and then a bombardier before his plane went down in the Pacific Ocean where he survived for 47 days lost at sea. He was eventually captured by the Japanese and terribly mistreated as a prisoner of war for two years. Zamperini was a known Olympic runner to his captors and often singled out and tortured daily. Yet, he persevered until the war ended in 1945. Immediately after the war, he had a difficult time dealing with all the experiences he endured in the war and turned to an alcohol addiction. However, he persevered and eventually found his Christian faith and a 12-step program which freed him from his alcoholism. He lived to be 97 years old. I believe this was partially due to his resilience and partially because of the faith he found in God after the war.

There are many other resilient individuals who have learned how to deal with stress and have lived long and healthy lives. Are you a resilient individual? I believe that I have exhibited resilience at times to overcome some of the challenges and stressors in my life. I have never faced anything close to Louis Zamperini, but I have had my share of stress and learned to persevere through these challenges while developing useful techniques to live a healthy life.

The L.E.A.R.N. Principles

Through my many trials, I have discovered the ideas that will help you reduce and manage your stress and improve your overall well-being. These are the L.E.A.R.N. principles. Each of the letters provides a strategy to help you keep your head above water and get you back on dry land with a sense of peace and serenity. These five principles will provide you with essential tools to keep your anxiety and distress under control while you live a healthy, active, and joy-filled life in a stressed-filled world.

L-AUGH
E-XERCISE
A-TTITUDE OF GRATITUDE & GIVING BACK
R-ELAX, R-EFLECT, R-ECHARGE
N-UTRITION

LAUGH

EXERCISE

ATTITUDE OF GRATITUDE &
GIVING BACK

RELAX, REFLECT, RECHARGE

NUTRITION

3

WHY LAUGHTER?

The first stress reduction principle is LAUGHTER. A sense of humor and the ability to laugh are important concepts for you to understand as you increase peace and lower stress in your life. I have been a professional clown for over 20 years. I have entertained both children and adults with my clown character, Silly Sally. I get so much joy bringing laughter to others. We find freedom when we let go, act silly, have fun, and stop worrying about what other people say or think. When we can laugh in stressful situations to lighten the mood or let our inner child out to play, those stress hormones diminish, and we can experience joy in the situation. Laughter has many of the same effects as exercise. When we have a good belly laugh, our blood pressure and the stress hormone cortisol lower, and our heart rates often rise. Additionally, we have a sense of release after we laugh really hard. In Rod Martin's article, *Is Laughter the Best Medicine? Humor, Laughter, and Physical Health*, he states, "Various authors have suggested, for example, that vigorous laughter exercises and relaxes muscles, improves respiration, stimulates circulation, increases the production of pain-killing endorphins, decreases the production of stress-related hormones, and enhances immunity." [12]

Laughter and crying come from the same deep part of us as we exhibit these emotions. Have you ever laughed so hard that you started to cry? Pretty soon you are laughing and crying and maybe even peeing your pants all at the same time! Hopefully, the peeing your pants laughter does not happen too often, but the ability to let loose and laugh and cry is good for your body and soul. The freedom to release those emotions can be therapeutic and allow the stress hormones to leave your system.

Truth is Funnier Than Fiction

One of the keys to laughing when stressed is to look for the humor in a situation. Often, truth is funnier than fiction if we look for the humor or try a little creativity to deal with an otherwise stressful situation. Have you ever watched people at the mall or at another place such as a fair, ballgame, or farmer's market? I do not advocate making fun of people, but there are some "interesting" things you can giggle about by observing what happens in real life. Better yet, learn to laugh at yourself. My clown friend, Jan, is good at this and always has funny stories to tell about real things that have happened to her. Once, she went shopping at Wal-Mart and needed to use the restroom. She utilized one of the provided paper seat-covers for added protection from germs. What she did not realize upon leaving the restroom, was that the paper seat cover got stuck inside the back of her pants. Jan left the restroom to shop in the store, then checked out, went out to her car, and drove home all the while not realizing the seat cover was still rustling behind her.

"As I was shopping, I could occasionally hear tissue paper rustling, but I paid no attention until I got out of the car in the garage, heard paper rustling louder, ran through the house to my full-length mirror, and their it was, circling my behind. I thought OMG!!! ...No wonder people were looking at me."

Can you imagine seeing her going through the store and NO ONE told her the seat cover was dragging behind her pants? Jan and others get a big chuckle out of that funny story now, but she was mortified at the time. Jan can live her life with a sense of humor, even when things are hard or stressful and can laugh at sometimes stressful or embarrassing situations that happen to her.

Because I am a clown, I have had numerous opportunities to laugh with others when I get to my gig location. But some of the funniest situations happen when I am on my way to a gig or after I am done with my paid assignment. When I am out and about in clown costume, I wish I had a dollar for every time someone asks me, "Are you out clowning around today?" I know the people who say that to me think it is an original, funny line, but I have heard that question more times than I can count. I admit it is pretty funny when I am out at the gas pump, using the "little clowns' room" in a convenience store or at a fast-food stop through the drive-through in my clown costume. I can use these everyday situations to play with others and have fun while spreading smiles and laughter in the most ordinary places.

Another funny story happened many years ago. After a gig entertaining with my clown friend Vickie, we stopped to get some food in our clown costumes. It was late in the evening at a local restaurant that has a walk-up window. Now, Vickie didn't have as much experience as I did working with or teaching teenage boys. As we were waiting for our food, a group of high school boys walked up beside us and waited in line to order. They asked us questions about being clowns. I am always careful when I am out in my clown costume as there are some people who just try to mess with me or on occasion have even crossed the line of swearing, throwing things at, or yelling at me just to see what I will do. On that evening, one of the boys asked Vickie if her nose squeaked and she told him, "No." He then asked her if he could touch her clown nose. As those words came out of his mouth, I was forming the words, "Don't let him do that." But before I could say it, she told him he could touch her nose. In a flash he grabbed her clown nose and ran off into the night to a nearby hotel parking lot. Vickie and I looked at each other and then I sprinted after him.

Of course, his friends thought this scene was hilarious, and I can laugh about it now. But, at the time, Silly Sally running at full speed in her big clown shoes and trying not to trip and fall while chasing a much faster high school boy, was not what I would call "a day at the circus." The restaurant manager called the police while I tried to find the kid. By the time the police showed up Vickie had made her way to the hotel as well. The officers discovered our nose thief had made his way to the back of the hotel where he was hiding from us "scary" clowns. The police made him get in the back of the squad car and told Vickie she could file assault charges against him. She decided that an apology and him getting placed in the squad car to think about his actions were enough. At the time, the incident was not funny, but now we both laugh about it. I am sure those boys, the police officers, and the restaurant staff have all had many chuckles about that clown nose incident over the years.

As an educator, I have dealt with some stressful situations, but I have also had the opportunity to utilize humor when things get tense at school. As an elementary physical education teacher, flexibility and the ability to go with the flow are important for me to maintain low stress levels. Years ago, right before Christmas break, I was teaching a kindergarten class. If you have been around an elementary school before Christmas, you are aware of the excitement and the level of difficulty in keeping students focused. My students were in the gym when suddenly, the security lights began to go on and off with no warning. This distracted the students, and they had a hard time following my directions. They kept asking why the lights were going on and off and watching the lights instead of practicing their skills. The creative teacher in me made up an elaborate story about how Santa was watching them and whenever those lights came on, his camera was zooming in from the North Pole so they should be following directions and do the right thing. That was just the information they needed to hear to keep them on-task for the remainder of the class. Afterward, they repeatedly asked when the Santa lights would be coming on again.

During COVID-19, it was especially helpful and important to laugh on a regular basis. Not that a pandemic was funny, but many things made me giggle. I also provided laughter for others during that stressful time by making funny videos, doing socially distanced telegrams, telling jokes, and sharing funny stories on social media and via email.

Humor in the Workplace

Creating laughter for others reduces stress and brings joy to people. In addition to my clown character, I also provide singing telegrams in a variety of costumes to adults. Many of these telegrams are in "cubicle farm" office settings. I strive to be in character from the moment I leave the car until I return which often allows me to play with people on my walk to the building. Many times, I have been in my big yellow chicken costume in a busy business district saying hello and waving to people as I make my way to the delivery location. I find it interesting that some adults can smile and play with me while others ignore my greeting and give no response as if there weren't a large chicken walking down the street. Once I enter the office area, I make my way to the recipient's cubicle. The recipient's co-workers stick their heads up out of their cubicles and chuckle at what is about to happen. Once I get to the recipient's desk, I say something to cause a chuckle, place a large balloon hat on their head, and proceed to do the chicken dance in the middle of the cubicles. People laugh and have a good time. Some recipients play along while others stand quietly embarrassed by my appearance.

One summer, I even did a telegram in my chicken costume at the Iowa State Fair campgrounds. My husband drove me through the campgrounds in our pickup while I stuck my head out the window, waved, and clucked to people. The funniest part was that this telegram was in 2015 when there was a huge bird flu outbreak, and no poultry could show at the fair that summer. I think I was the only chicken permitted to appear at the fair which added additional laughter points for the recipient.

Being able to help others laugh for a moment during a stressful workday is fun and rewarding. Perhaps, you have fun at work, help others laugh and bring a positive vibe to your workplace. Humor and laughter in the work setting helps productivity and retains long-term employees. Humor and laughter bond work groups and make work cultures more fun and enjoyable. "Nine out of ten people say they are more productive when they're around positive people."[13] Think about the jobs you have held where you were able to laugh and have fun. You likely felt more a part of the group and were more motivated to complete your work. In the article *Humor and Group Effectiveness* by Romero & Pescosolido, they stated, "Humor supports group viability through its role in creating positive affect, fostering group cohesion, and reducing employee turnover."[14] So, if you add some laughter to your next group discussion or activity, you might help you and your co-workers reduce stress and get more done.

Laughter and Online Dating

As I mentioned, I was single for a long time which at times was stressful and discouraging. I found it hard to meet compatible single Christian men. So, I combed the personal ads and then eventually tried online dating. I encountered some "interesting" men who were looking for love, and I met dozens of those guys before I found my husband, Paul. Many times, I would sit and laugh as I read the profiles or after I met someone on a blind date.

I did meet some genuinely nice "normal" guys, but we did not match up. I would say 80 percent of the men I met were what I will call "socially illiterate," and I had a few good laughs. I will share a few of my experiences because I always said I should write a book about my 25 years of looking for a man in the personal ads and online.

I often spent my Saturday nights exploring various online dating sites. I copied some of the profiles over the years and they made me laugh. I found odd what some of these men posted in their dating profiles considering they were trying to make a good impression on potential dates. I am not trying to be judgmental in posting these ads. Rather, I want to illustrate how I was able to find humor in a sometimes-frustrating process. Eventually, I found my husband, Paul, on one of these dating sites. It was certainly a God thing in how He brought us together as we lived six hours apart. Here are a few examples of the personal ads that I copied directly with grammatical errors intact.

The first match was a 37-year-old never-married unemployed man who was obviously a bit of a nerd. He could be a character on the TV show, **The Big Bang Theory**. Here is his profile:

> *"Me and My Ideal Match" I am an unemployed actor living at home in my parent's basement. When not attending Sci-Fi conventions or gaming, you can find me at the local comic bookstores. My lifetime goal is to meet William Shatner, but so*

far, I've only met some guy who played a red shirted crewman in TOS. I spend as much time on the internet as I can, and sometimes more. I don't currently have an account on here, so don't expect a reply (unless you really really interest me; do you speak Klingon?)."

No, I don't speak Klingon, so needless to say I didn't respond to this ad. Grin!

Another profile from a 38-year-old never-married volunteer firefighter's profile still makes me chuckle:

"In our free time, my ideal match and I would explore each other's physical needs in order to see what turns each of other on. The feature that captures my attention is a woman's back side from her hips to her knees."

Mmm, maybe he is the man who called me on the phone and asked if he could come over right away to take a bath with me. Are you serious?

Check out this description that caught me by surprise.

"I am looking for a helpmate who will know they were called by God to me. CAUTION: Due to medical malfeasance I cannot have sexual intercourse, but I do really love to cuddle and rub backs. I hope that is pleasing enough."

Seriously?? CAUTION — I am concerned about this person that he would post this private information on a dating profile.

The smiles were not restricted to the written profiles. Among what seemed like hundreds of blind dates I endured, I had some funny or "interesting" experiences with men. Most of the time, I met guys at restaurants. I made sure I had my own transportation in case I encountered an issue, or I needed to leave. On one date, I met a guy at a restaurant, and we were sitting in a booth across from each other. Suddenly, he had dropped his napkin and was upside down with his feet up in the air as he retrieved his napkin. I barely kept myself from laughing out loud.

On another date at a restaurant, I was visiting with a man and thought we were having a nice conversation. About 30 minutes into our date, he abruptly said, "Well, I need to go now and check on my generator." Apparently, I had not made a good impression because his generator was turning him on more than I had.

There were a few guys that I dated more than once. Our initial date had gone well, and we had things in common. "B" was a guy I went out with for a couple of months. However, he was notoriously late — even on our first date. This was before the days of cell phones so often I waited up to an hour for him to show up at our destination. I am a person who values being on-time, so this lateness irritated me. One time, we were to meet at a movie theater about halfway between our locations which was about 25 minutes from his house. At the time, he still lived at home with his parents. I arrived at the theater at our agreed upon meeting time and waited in my car for him to show up. Shortly thereafter, his mom drove into the parking lot and informed me that "B" would be late, and I shouldn't leave. Who would send their mom to meet their date? Needless to say, this chronic lateness annoyed me. That, among some other issues between us, motivated me to stop seeing him. So, I kept looking for Mr. Right. Years later while I was doing a clown gig, I saw "B" again. He had **no** idea who I was, and I didn't tell him as I watched him interact with his daughter.

Now, I laugh at these dating experiences even though at the time some were stressful or depressing. I remember the time I was to meet another guy at the front of a restaurant. He had given me the description of his car and his general appearance. When I saw who I assumed was him coming toward the door, I greeted him.

"Hello are you, 'T'?" I asked.

"No," he said and quickly entered the restaurant bar area. No other man showed up. When I called his number, he didn't answer and never contacted me again. So, I am sure the guy who entered the restaurant was indeed, "T." He took one look at me and decided Silly Sally wasn't for him.

Then, I met Paul online, and we clicked. We dated long-distance for a while as we lived about six hours apart, but eventually he moved to Iowa where I reside. We were married in our late 40's. God is good!

I dated a lot of Mr. Wrongs before Paul came along. My mom was elated that I **finally** found my soul mate. Before we got engaged, Paul asked my mom if it would be OK to ask me to marry him. After she said yes and he was about to leave her house, my mom said, "I hope she says yes." My mom often says things that make me giggle. Shortly after our wedding, she said "Well, I can die now because I got to see you get married." Laughter is good, and my mom has lived to see Paul and I married nine years.

The Spiritual Side of Laughter

Experiencing laughter can have spiritual side effects as well. Have you ever laughed so hard that you cannot stop? I call this holy laughter. To me this is a spiritual, joyful experience. I am not referring to the charismatic fallen slain in the spirit kind of laughter, although some people might experience that in their churches. I am talking about when I laugh so hard that I can't stop for a while, and then I feel a total sense of release and joy.

To experience this kind of laughter, I believe you must experience holy laughter with others you trust while you let go of your inhibitions without alcohol or drugs involved. When you experience this joyful, holy laughter, you cannot help but decrease the stress that might have been weighing on you. Paul and I laugh a lot together! I believe this is so important to reduce stress in our marriage and create fun and joy in our relationship. When I participate in holy laughter, I am often around Paul. I have also experienced it with friends and co-workers particularly when we have been on a retreat or away from daily stressors. This laughter might start with something simple and then spread among the group members because it is contagious. Have you watched any laughing baby videos lately? You cannot help but start laughing and smiling yourself. So, surround yourself with others who like to laugh, as you will find it hard to not join in the laughter.

Laughter Yoga

When it comes to laughter, sometimes, you may just have to fake it until you make it. I became a certified laughter leader in 2006 through an organization called the World Laughter Tour. Laughter exercises or laughter yoga was started in the mid 1990's by Dr. Madan Kataria. These simulated exercises guide participants through different ways to laugh. The idea is that the brain and body do not know the difference between when you fake a laugh and when you laugh for real at something you find really funny. This simulated laughter is contagious and can lead to stimulated or authentic laughter. The laughter and deep breathing increase oxygen flow in the body and brain and energize participants while they reduce stress. Many laughter clubs have opened around the world, and people gather to participate in these sometimes-ridiculous looking laughter exercises. But I can confirm, both as a participant and leader of these funny exercises, participants feel better and are more joyful after they partake in these laughter gatherings.

I have faked a smile or a laugh when I have suddenly been stressed out or have been around someone who has that Debbie Downer personality. If someone is negative around me for a period of time, I will leave the room and go smile a few times in front of the bathroom mirror before I return to the negative person. This usually helps me to feel better and improves my own attitude. Otherwise, I can get sucked into the hole of Debbie Downer's negative talk and complaints. You must recognize when others are influencing you negatively. This can cause you stress and depression if you are not careful to distance yourself from the situation. If you can't slip away, a good question to ask the person dragging you down is, "What is something positive that has happened to you today, or what are you grateful for today?" This might help to redirect Debbie Downer back to a more positive tone. If this doesn't work, then it is time for you to step away and surround yourself with more positive people in your life, or soon you will become Debbie's twin brother or sister.

Laughter and Healing

Laughter can also affect our immune system and the healing process. I am a firm believer in the proverb, "Laughter is the best medicine." The idea of being merry or joyful and how that affects our health goes back to Biblical times. "A cheerful heart is good medicine, but a crushed spirit dries up the bones." Proverbs 17:22 NIV. When we laugh or rejoice about something, our bodies and brains respond positively. The medical community has recognized the physiological and psychological power of laughter. In the book, *Anatomy of an Illness*,[15] Norman Cousins recounts how he successfully recovered from a serious illness utilizing laughter as a part of his self-healing. Cousins was diagnosed with Ankylosing Spondylitis, a degenerative condition of the connective tissue in his spine. His doctors gave him a 1-in-500 chance of recovery. Cousins recognized that stress had compromised his immune system. Additionally, he might have been experiencing adrenal fatigue or chronic stress which could have contributed to his contracting this disease.

He added laughter and a change to his nutrition and attitude to his healing process. "I made the joyous discovery that ten minutes of genuine belly laughter had an anesthetic effect and would give me at least two hours of pain-free sleep."[16] To help relieve his pain, Cousins watched funny movies before bed or when he woke up. "The laughter routine was in full force. I was completely off drugs and sleeping pills. Sleep — blessed, natural sleep without pain — was becoming increasingly prolonged. At the end of the eighth day, I was able to move my thumbs without pain. There was no doubt in my mind that I was going to make it back all the way."

Patch Adams, M.D. is well known for his use of laughter and humor. As his clown character, he helps patients, their families, or caregivers in hospitals as well as on overseas mission trips. He often gathers other clowns for trips overseas to cheer up and bring love and hope to orphanages, hospitals, and places where people are forgotten. In his book, *House Calls*[17] Adams, "recommends that you can maintain your health with joy, laughter, and kindness. Patch also suggests that sometimes the most helpful treatment is hope, love and relaxation, and the simple joy of living." R.A. Martin writes that having a sense of humor "may enable individuals to cope more effectively with stress by allowing them to gain perspective and distance themselves from a stressful situation, enhancing their feelings of mastery and well-being in the face of adversity." [18] When we can laugh about a stressful situation and let things go, we reduce that stress on the spot. Think about it. It is difficult to be stressed and upset when you're laughing or smiling. I am not advocating that we minimize serious situations or pretend they are not real or important. I believe we can reduce a lot of our stress when we can try and see the humor in it.

I have a good clown friend, Pam, who went through the stressful and heart-breaking loss of her husband to cancer. During much of his treatment for three years, they were able to bring humor and laughter to help themselves and the medical staff that treated him. They shed a lot of tears, but humor played a huge role in their cancer journey. They joked and laughed during Rick's chemotherapy treatments and brought laughter to the staff. At one appointment, when Rick had lost all his hair, he donned a funny spiked blue rubber piece on his head and placed a ball cap on top before the doctor came in to see him. During his appointment, Rick told the doctor that the chemo was having a terrible effect on his hair as removed the cap and revealed the blue spiked hair on the top of his head. Here is what Pam said in one of her blog posts during his treatment.

"As you already know, humor runs freely in our home ... or wherever we are. I can't tell you how many times this past year we have found ourselves laughing through our tears, literally. We strongly believe that our faith and love of humor has sustained Rick with such a GREAT quality of life thus far. Humor is a coping tool for me and can also sometimes be a "shield" from hurt. Regardless of its place, it is definitely working for both of us!"

The day Rick died Pam was even able to find humor in his passing. The morning of his death, she discovered their refrigerator had stopped working. They even talked about how she would need to pick out a new one. Shortly after that conversation, Rick died before Pam was able to do anything about the fridge. Her neighbor lady arranged for a new fridge and had it delivered after Pam was back home that evening. When the delivery drivers arrived with the new refrigerator, here is how Pam reacted when they came into her house.

"I found out some time later that one of the delivery guys came out of the house and asked Karol, "When did her husband die?" She replied, just this morning. Apparently, I

had made the comment, "My husband died today and took the fridge with him!" He was speechless. But for some of you who knew Rick best … you might agree with that statement. We always joked that we would put his famous saying, "If you don't eat – you'll die" on his headstone. Well, we didn't … but this story makes me grin."

Pam coped with much of their cancer stress by infusing humor into a lot of their journey. She still brings laughter and smiles to many others as she plays at her performances. She even entertains airline and hotel staff when she travels. I try to emulate this playfulness whenever I can, but Pam deserves an award for her spontaneous sense of humor and the many laughs and smiles she brings to others. In the next chapter, we will discover that play and laughter are not just for kids.

Silly Sally performing on stage. Photo credit Christine Carroll

Silly Sally helps others laugh and play as she performs singing telegrams in her chicken costume. Photo credit: Renee McLaughlin

4

HAVE YOU PLAYED TODAY?

One of the critical parts of the laughter principle is the ability to play. My clown friend Pam demonstrated the benefits of living life with a sense of humor in chapter 3. When was the last time you connected with your inner child to play when alcohol was not involved?

What is Play?

When we play, we let go of the social conditioning of our years of schooling and the socialization process as we grew into adults. Society crushes the creative inner child in most of us as we go through elementary school. This is especially true now that standardized testing is at the forefront of K-12 education. Unlike previous generations of students, kindergartners in the United States rarely play, nap, socialize and have fun during school hours. Now, many must learn hundreds of sight words by the end of their kindergarten year in addition to required math facts. Time for fantasy play, recess, and social skills has been dismissed or diminished in favor of more math and reading blocks.

Not only is this developmentally inappropriate, but children are not given many opportunities for free play where they can learn about the world around them. In my opinion, academia stifles their inner child replaces it with what some adults perceive as important standardized testing. Children are discouraged from laughing or having fun and expected to sit still and listen to adults. I suggest that part of being able to laugh freely is getting the chance to play. When we don't play, our mood might darken because we are missing the joy that play provides. Children naturally laugh more easily than adults and often at amazingly simple things. We adults can learn if we observe how young children play or better yet play with them!

With my clown character, Silly Sally, I often entertain children with puppets. Many times, the puppet does a funny gesture or makes a funny sound, and the children burst into laughter while many of the adults sit stone-faced. A sense of humor is more of a learned response over time, and our past childhood experiences affect how we react to current situations and life. "Humor is the quality that makes something funny."[19] When someone has a sense of humor and does not take life too seriously, they can play along and roll with the punches rather than getting stressed. They don't get their panties in a bunch, so to speak. Can you recall when you spent time with someone with a good sense of humor, and they were able to lighten a stressful moment? My guess is that it made that moment less stressful for you as well.

Play Relieves Stress

So, why is play so important for all of us to help relieve stress and help our brains? In Stuart Brown's book, **_Play-How it shapes the Brain, Opens the imagination, and invigorates the Soul_**, [20] he states that "Play is a very primal activity. One of the hallmarks of play is that anyone can do it." The brain needs play to develop and grow. "As children, our reward for play is strong because we need it to help generate a rapidly developing brain." Play encourages neural connections in the brain. "Active play selectively stimulates brain-derived neurotropic factor (which stimulates nerve growth) in the amygdala (where emotions get processed) and the dorsolateral prefrontal cortex (where executive decisions are processed)." Play itself may be purposeless and allow children and adults a way to lose track of time. But Brown states that "Play is an absorbing, apparently purposeless activity that provides enjoyment and a suspension of self-consciousness and sense of time. It is also self-motivating and makes you want to do it again."

Children, Play, and Creativity

As a child, I spent hundreds of hours in free and fantasy play either by myself or with my siblings, cousins, or peers. I remember playing outside on our acreage. I sang to the animals and played in the barn or in the sandbox under the big red maple tree. On many summer days, I tied a rope to the outside valve of the propane tank, climbed up the side and sat on top pretending that I was riding a horse across the wild west. It is a wonder I did not cause a propane leak and explosion during my many cowgirl adventures on that horse I now call "Gassy" in the barnyard! In another adventurous play activity, I climbed on top of hog barn to view our pasture, cars on the highway, and soak in the southern sun. Then, I jumped off the roof and landed somewhere amongst the pigs. I certainly wasn't afraid of heights back then!

When we moved to another town and I was no longer living out in the country, I still spent most of my free time playing outside or being creative indoors. It was not uncommon to find me in homemade costumes created by my mother any time of the year. I developed and performed shows with my friends, siblings, or with my cousins and reveled in many creative opportunities in elementary school. I learned in creative ways and had special teachers who encouraged and designed lessons that sparked my creative talents. In upper elementary and middle school, my friend

Denise and I created songs, films, recipes, and many other things that we shared with our families and at school. During the energy crisis of the 1970's, we composed "The Energy Song," and we performed it at a school-wide middle school assembly. I can still play it on the piano. Denise is now a successful professional musician in New York City who still creates, plays, and performs music! It is sad to me that children today are not given as many opportunities to be creative and play as I had during my childhood.

Our factory model of many schools and the movement toward standards discourages creativity, play and imagination. Instead, it socializes kids to stand in line and walk quietly while they conform to the right answers. By the time most children start middle school, they have forgotten how to unleash their imaginations and are less comfortable being silly. Many kids are socialized into "the right and appropriate" way to behave and answer questions which seldom includes the freedom to laugh and have fun in school. In Ken Robinson's book, **Creative Schools**[21], he states "The standards movement favors direct instruction of factual information and skills and whole-class teaching rather than group activities. When it comes to assessment, the standards movement emphasizes formal, written examination and extensive use of multiple-choice tests so that students' answers can be easily codified and processed." All this testing combined with the extensive amount of time children spend on screens influences the amount of time they spend in free play and increases stress on the brain. In my opinion, if children are not given adequate opportunities to play and be creative, they might experience higher stress levels.

As mentioned above, children provide much laughter and are experts on play. As a teacher, one of my many responsibilities at school is recess duty. I enjoy going out and doing recess duty because it gives me time to observe and listen to children at play without much adult interference.

Kids, by nature, are creative and imaginative souls, and the ideas and fun they have at recess often bring me a smile and laughter. In the warmer months, they play tag, imaginative games, or spend time looking for lady bugs among other fun activities. During winter, they make snow forts, slide down the hills, and build snowmen with smiles on their faces. You may not be able to observe 75-100 kids all playing at the same time as I can, but you can take time to watch your own children or the kids at the local park or swimming pool. Spend time with your kids at school during recess and pay attention to what happens. When they are free and in a state of uninterrupted play, notice how they truly express joy. You will get a few chuckles along the way. You will also learn how they reduce stress through play. Additionally, you will observe how they participate in much-needed exercise to allow their brains to recharge after all the academic learning in the classroom.

The Importance of Outside Play

Outside play time at home is important for children as well, but I am concerned this is being replaced with time spent on screens and devices. Playtime helps children and adults process and deal with stress. The idea of free-range kids is disappearing, and their time being creative and imaginative is being replaced by video games, movies, videos, and structured activities. Some parents may want to keep their children inside out of safety concerns. However, replacing outside play with screens and devices rather than encouraging free play keeps the brain and body from processing stress. It also keeps them from getting much needed physical exercise. Participation in daily free play for preschool and elementary children is an important developmental stage that all kids should experience. In their book *A Moving Child is a Learning Child*,[22] Authors Gill Connell and Cheryle McCarthy state, "Play produces children capable of pure joy, deep reasoning, and ideas nobody's ever thought of. And by any means, that's a start in life worthy of our children."

Prior to moving out to the country in 2019 near a college community of about 60,000 people in central Iowa, I lived in that town. My neighborhood was close to the campus and was a typical suburban community with many families who had young children. I spent a lot of time outside in my neighborhood walking, jogging, or biking and rarely saw children outside playing. When I go into town now and drive through neighborhoods, I observe kids outside playing in the parks or in their own yards infrequently. This has changed in the years since I was a kid in the 1960's and 70's.

Many years ago, children were outside **all** the time until dark especially during the summer. Kids created their own entertainment with friends. They played games, had fun, created things, rode bikes for hours without either helmets or adult supervision! These social interactions and free time for children are disappearing and, in my opinion, cause major stress, social, emotional and developmental problems for our kids and adults. When children are on devices and screens, they are often sitting passively or participating in violent gaming instead of playing and interreacting with others and experiencing social time, joy, and laughter.

Maybe you had few creative opportunities or spent too many hours on screens rather than in free fantasy play when you were a child. Perhaps, it has been a long time since you have let your inner child out to play, to be creative, and therefore you are a hot mess with stress right now.

How Can You Play?

Let's figure out some ways you could laugh and play. What activity or hobby gives you joy? What helps you feel free and at peace? Where do you lose track of time? When you are in that state, I believe you do not feel stress but rather joy because your brain's feel-good endorphins are firing at a rapid pace. Whatever that activity is for you, take time to do it! Play helps you keep your head above water because it brings you joy and reduces stress. I do think many adults have difficulty with being free, laughing and letting themselves play and have fun. They have forgotten how to be carefree because of life circumstances and stress. Some people fill their time with devices and screens instead of having quiet time and reflection. We will talk more about reflection and quiet time in Chapter 6.

Laughter and play are an important part of helping you to keep your head above water and live with less stress in your life. But it will take effort on your part to get back to your inner child to allow yourself to laugh and play.

Action Steps for adding more laughter and infusing play to relieve stress:

1. Pay attention to the world around you and there shall be humor. Your attitude has a lot to do with this step and how you react to things that happen each day. Can you find some humor in and laugh at the stressful situations you encounter?

2. Fake it until you make it! If you are not finding ways to laugh by being stimulated with something you find funny, then fake a smile or a laugh. Remember, your body and brain don't know the difference between when you laugh at something you find funny or when you simulate or fake laughter. This is where a laughter yoga club can be helpful either in person or online including my YouTube channel.

3. Watch funny movies, YouTube videos, live entertainment or read funny books, comics, or joke and pay attention to what makes you laugh and why.

4. Hang out with people who are funny and can play. Observe them, ask questions, and play along.
5. Spend time observing children and play with them.
6. Play and be silly with your pets or watch funny pet videos.
7. Think back to how you played as a child. What gave you joy and where did you lose track of time? Could you try that activity again?

Laugh

EXERCISE

Attitude of gratitude &
giving back

Relax, Reflect, Recharge

Nutrition

5

EXERCISE – DO I REALLY HAVE TO DO THAT TODAY

As we move through the L.E.A.R.N. principles, the next way you can relieve stress and improve your well-being is through exercise. The many late night and daytime infomercials that explain how you can lose weight quickly without exercising should tell you many Americans obsess over figuring out ways to look good while avoiding exercise. Try a Google search for, "losing weight without exercising" and notice all the products and ideas that appear. Many people do not like to exercise or want to do it regularly. A large majority of individuals fail to see the benefits of moving their bodies beyond walking from the car to the fast-food restaurant or getting out of the car by using the drive-thru window. I did not write this book to shame you into exercising more. But I do want to inform you of the health benefits of a regular exercise program. Moreover, exercise is a key component in keeping your head above water.

Here is a short list of the benefits of exercise:
1. Enhance longevity and quality of life over a life span by decreasing your risks for many debilitating diseases

2. Enhance brain function to learn better in school and perform job duties or everyday tasks more efficiently
3. Decrease stress hormone levels
4. Decrease dementia risk by up to 50 percent. (Alzheimer's Research & Prevention Foundation)
5. Enhance mood and decrease depression

You are likely aware of the health risks when you do not exercise beyond your daily tasks. Our increasingly sedentary lifestyles combined with poor diets are slowly killing many adults. In fact, I have heard that a sedentary lifestyle is now the new smoking habit. The health risks of smoking cigarettes have been documented for several decades and thankfully, many people have quit. Many public places make it nearly impossible for a smoker to light up these days which is a good thing especially for us nonsmokers. But in my opinion, the looming health risks are prolonged inactivity and poor nutritional choices. In combination, failure to exercise regularly beyond daily tasks and/or an unhealthy diet contribute to many preventable health issues such as heart disease, stroke, cancer, and type II diabetes. Also, as stated in number 4 above, a regular exercise regimen can cut the risks of developing dementia by 50 percent. We will talk more about the effects of exercise on the brain later in this chapter. But let's establish the current state of inactivity and obesity in America.

The Data on Exercise

According to the Centers for Disease Control report[23], 25 percent of adults do not participate in any physical or leisure activities. The good news is that nearly 50 percent of adults report meeting the minimum requirements for aerobic physical activity. The other 25 percent of adults are participating in more vigorous physical activities. Keep in mind that this data is based on a survey where adults self-reported their physical activity level. In my opinion, the percentage of adults living a sedentary lifestyle is likely higher than reported by the CDC especially given the statistics of people who are obese and overweight.

The CDC reports that nearly 40 percent of adults are overweight and obese in the US.[24] That's over 93 million adults who are living with this condition. Nearly 19 percent of our children ages 2-19 are considered overweight or obese with 25 percent of our teens dealing with this condition. This is the first generation of children who could have a shorter lifespan than their parents! We now have children with type II diabetes because of poor dietary choices and inactivity. This rarely happened in the past.

In 2020 while writing this book, new projections by state for the prevalence of obesity by the year 2030 were released. *Projected US State-Level Prevalence of Adult Obesity and Severe Obesity*[25]

Using data pertaining to the percentage obesity prevalence in the US since 1990, researchers predicted what might happen by 2030 given the upward trend of body mass index (BMI) numbers. The researchers forecast that nearly one in two adults (48.9 percent) in the US will be obese, and many states will have an average over 50 percent by the year 2030. Given the health consequences of obesity, without changes, our nation is on its way toward a healthcare crisis!

It's Never Too Late to Start Exercising

There is good news! It is **never** too late to start to move your body if you physically can. Even if you can only move while sitting in a chair, you can increase your physical activity level. I have worked in the wellness field my entire career with people of all ages and abilities from preschoolers through senior citizens. It is my life mission to help others live a healthy, active lifestyle. I have witnessed how regular physical activity can affect people's personal and mental health including my own.

Years ago, I worked as an exercise instructor/supervisor at a county hospital in a new wellness program. I developed exercise regimens and supervised adults on exercise equipment in small classes. I also motivated and coached them. Many of the people who came to our classes had cardiac issues, chronic pain, or other disabilities. Most did not exercise regularly before they started the program.

One participant, Genevieve, was in her 80's and began attending one of my classes. When she started, she was bent over, and could barely walk on the treadmill. She needed assistance with much of the routine. Over the course of six months, I watched Genevieve go from a weak little old lady to a confident participant who showed immense growth in her cardiovascular endurance and muscle strength. By the end of the exercise class, she walked briskly, exhibited increased muscle tone, and had confidence in her abilities. Plus, she enjoyed coming to class where she had the opportunity to socialize with others. I can't say for sure that Genevieve lived longer because she started coming to our classes, but I did see vast improvement in someone who had previously exercised very little. It's never too late to start exercising!

The Hunt Study published in 2008[26], in the *European Journal of Preventive Cardiology* followed Norwegian adults with coronary artery disease for 18 years. As the researchers followed these patients over the longitudinal study, they discovered that exercise training reduced the mortality rate in both men and women. Another study published in the *Journal of the American College of Cardiology* concluded that exercise helps us live longer.[27] The 15-year study followed over 55,000 adults ages 18-100 and discovered that by running just 5-10 minutes per day at slow speeds they "markedly reduced risks of death from all causes and cardiovascular disease." You don't have to be an elite athlete to gain benefits from moving your body each day.

A regular exercise routine can help prevent stress-related diseases such as heart disease and stroke. When you exercise, you reap other physical benefits like a lower resting heart rate, lower blood pressure, better lung capacity, better sleep, and more energy. Exercise is also highly beneficial for your brain.

Dr. John Medina has developed 12 principles that he calls *Brain Rules*.[28] Did you know that humans were not created to be sedentary? Historically, we humans were on the move much of our days. "From an evolutionary perspective, our brains developed while we walked or ran as many as 12 miles a day. The brain still craves that experience, especially in sedentary populations like our own. That's why exercise boosts brain power in such populations."

I seldom walk 12 miles a day doing my everyday tasks on a consistent basis. However, I prioritize time each day to exercise my body beyond daily tasks because I recognize the benefits for both my body and brain. The bottom line is that if you want to live longer, be less stressed and have a higher quality life, you incorporate exercise into your daily routine. I know this is not an easy lifestyle to prioritize especially given all our distractions and required tasks, but this habit does not have to take hours. Think about where you can sneak in daily two or three ten-minute stints of brisk walking or ten minutes of strength and balance exercises.

Get Started With an Exercise Routine

I try to get at least 30 minutes of exercise each day. I also track my steps to be sure I get a minimum of 10,000 steps daily. Maybe, for you, 5,000 steps are a more reasonable goal. Whatever your ability, set some goals and get moving. If you can't walk, maybe you can do water exercises or ride a stationary bike. Join a class with others who have abilities like yours and find an accountability partner. Turn on one of the hundreds of possible exercise videos on YouTube or other places online. I have several available on my website: www.dolifewellnow.com

For my own personal exercise routine, I find it best to do it first thing in the morning. I must get up 30 minutes earlier than if I did not take time to exercise. I believe the benefits make the early rising time worthwhile. First, aerobic exercise wakes me up as it gets the blood flowing and oxygenates my brain and body. If I wake up in a bad mood or do not sleep well, the exercise usually resets my mindset and boosts my energy level. Second, this exercise time early in the morning also gives me a 30-minute block of quiet time for prayer, meditation, and reflection which I will discuss more in Chapter 7. So, my exercise routine allows me to also get in my quiet time before I start looking at emails, text messages, social media, or TV. This regimen starts my morning in a positive way and prepares me to face the day. This was especially helpful during lockdown when the media was full of negative and discouraging COVID-19 news. I started my days with positivity through exercise, prayer, and quiet time.

Although I am a wellness professional, I also have days when I don't feel like getting up and exercising. I have been doing this long enough to know that once I get going, I will feel better physically and emotionally. I realize the far-reaching benefits of exercise go beyond physically feeling better and/or helping me to have a better quality of life. I often tell myself that exercising on a regular basis is my nursing home insurance. Are you still not convinced to get yourself moving?

Exercise, Stress, and the Brain

Many of the neurological benefits of exercise are being discovered. Nearly every person reading this book can improve brain function by participating in an exercise routine.

Exercise is one of the best ways to keep your head above water! In Dr. John Ratey's book, **Spark, *The Revolutionary New Science of Exercise and the Brain*[29]**, he discusses the importance of the mind-body connection. He examines how exercise improves brain functions and efficiency, decreases stress, and helps students focus more in the classroom. Dr. Ratey states that, "Regular aerobic activity calms the body, so that it can handle more stress before the serious response involving heart rate and stress hormones kick in." Personally, I find that when I am stressed, it helps to take a walk or do something physical. Exercise focuses my elevated state of mind. It also helps me process the stress, calms my brain, and assists me to refocus on how to best respond to the stressful situation.

A side benefit when you exercise with others is that you also derive the social interaction and accountability from being around other people. Loneliness is a problem for many adults, especially our senior population and those who live alone. In the many senior exercise classes I have taught, the social interaction, fun, and conversation among participants are as important as the exercise routines. Many seniors who live alone thrive in these group classes. I have observed that they stick to their exercise habits because they have group accountability.

Exercise, Learning, and Productivity

In the last twenty years, numerous research studies have focused on how being physically active affects brain function. In 1999, a study revealed that exercise grows new brain cells.[30]

This is great news for all of us, especially older adults! The brain responds to exercise in many wonderful ways. Ratey[31] states that "exercise improves learning on three levels:

1. It optimizes your mind-set to improve alertness, attention, and motivation.

2. It prepares and encourages nerve cells to bind to one another which is the cellular basis for logging in new information.
3. Spurs the development of new nerve cells from the hippocampus."

In addition to making your body stronger, living longer, and preventing disease, when you exercise you improve your brain function. When you get that brisk walk in, your brain will focus better and process information more efficiently.

We think better after a bout of exercise, and this is not limited to adults. Children benefit academically from being physically active. A 2009 study at the University of Illinois involving nine-year-olds revealed that children achieved better school-based academic performance after they walked for 20 minutes on a treadmill. The study showed "Acute bouts of moderately-intense aerobic exercise (i.e., walking) may improve the cognitive control of attention in preadolescent children, and further supports the use of moderate acute exercise as a contributing factor for increasing attention and academic performance." Using a brain scan, researchers also observed that as a result of walking, the children's brains had more brain activity in comparison with their brains at rest. [32]

Exercise and Learning in Schools

In my experiences working with children, I have observed that when students move after sitting while working on schoolwork, they focus better and remain calmer. Unfortunately, with the emphasis on standardized testing since 2002, American schools have been required to implement 90-minute blocks of literacy and math training at the elementary level. This is a result of the US government's 2002 *No Child Left Behind* Act now known as *The Elementary and Secondary Education Act*. Recess and physical education have been reduced and replaced with more seat work. In my opinion, these changes have been disastrous for our American schools. I believe all this testing and more time required for reading and math has resulted in higher stress levels for both children and teachers. At the same time, it has not significantly improved proficiency on the tests or academic achievement.

Along with many other complicated problems facing our schools including a breakdown of the family unit, many schools are struggling to stay above water. Thus, one way to help schools keep students engaged and learning is to keep or add more opportunities for students to move throughout the school day. We can accomplish this if we maintain and/or add recess time, physical education, art and music as well as designated brain breaks or wakes (intentionally getting students up and moving) during academic block times. Many students, especially younger children, are kinesthetic learners who need to process learning and new information through their bodies. We will keep students' brains engaged and activated if we provide more project-based learning activities, small group work, and creative projects. Students at every age benefit because they are doing more than just worksheets and seat work.

To help the brain and body develop and prepare for academic learning, younger children should focus on basic motor, social, and balance skills. Instead, political and parental pressure in the United States is to teach children to start reading and learning math facts at younger and younger ages. Some students are not ready to process these academic skills until ages 7 or 8. In fact, many places around the world such as Finland, Sweden, Singapore, and many African countries do not start their students in formal school training until later when their brains are more ready to take in the information.

I visit a lot of early childhood centers and have been teaching basic motor skills to preschoolers for 30+ years. In addition, I have many other opportunities to observe, entertain, and teach young children. Much of the formal schooling in the United States has shifted during my professional teaching career toward learning academic skills such as requirements for learning sight words and math facts by the end of kindergarten.

It is my observation that many children are more restless, have trouble concentrating, are frustrated and exhibit more stress and have more behavioral issues with all this academic pressure than in the past. I believe they need to play, practice large and fine motor skills, cross their midlines (The midline is an imaginary line drawn down the entire body and separates the left and right sides. Therefore, you cross the midline when you move your arms or legs across the body's midline to the opposite side.) and have opportunities to be creative and socialize through free play. I have observed early childhood educators struggle to teach young children to sit and do higher-thinking academic skills rather than engaging children in creative and dramatic play, movement activities, and learning social skills. The educators are usually not at fault but are required to do so by the federal government and state mandates. In many cases, parents also pressure educators to teach these skills to their preschool students.

For example, since 2014, kindergartners and all other grade levels in my state have required reading skills testing three times a year. Thirty years ago, the skills kindergartners are currently tested on used to be taught in first grade. Many preschoolers are being tested on their reading skills. In many classrooms, table time for academic practice has replaced play centers, recess time, and social skill development time. Kindergarten used to focus on social skills, creative play, and motor development.

That is no longer the case. When we combine this with the many devices parents allow their children to use including violent video games, it is no wonder many of our young children struggle academically, socially, physically, and emotionally. We need to take a step back and re-evaluate these changes in education along with how technology affects students. We must allow children time to learn basic life skills and move their bodies through their day. I believe this decrease in play and exercise with the added increase in screen time in early childhood is detrimental to the brain and body. When children lack these important developmental opportunities for play and exercise, this can lead to chronic stress, changes in the brain and a decrease in overall well-being as they grow into adulthood.

Brain Wakes

Many adults can benefit by taking brain wakes or breaks during their time at work especially those who spend a great deal of time sitting at their jobs and looking at computer screens. During COVID-19, many kids and adults worked or met remotely via a screen. This change in how we work and learn might influence how many of us do our jobs and attend school long into the future. What can you do to feel better, relieve stress, and be more productive while on all these screens?

You can improve your work efficiency and productivity by taking a short break every 20-30 minutes. A quick brain wake or break is when you take one minute to stand up, stretch, walk around the room, and refocus your eyes off the screen. Once or twice an hour, take a 5-to-10-minute walk while processing your work or talking to a co-worker about something you're working on together. I call this "walk and talk" which can be done on a phone while you walk if you are not working in the same office as your co-worker. This will help you be more creative, brainstorm ideas, and work more collaboratively.

I forced myself to get up and move while I wrote this book. As a result, each time I got up, moved and took a break, I came back with more ideas and better focus on my concepts for the book. Adults can only pay attention to something for about 17-20 minutes before they need to refocus by talking to a colleague or change something up so the brain can attune better. For children, we can use their age in minutes as a gauge of how long they can realistically focus before they need to do something new. For example, a five-year-old can only focus for about five minutes before something needs to change beyond monotonous instruction time. The change could be something small. For example, the teacher can change up his/her voice or put on some music, use a prop, puppet, picture or change to a different activity entirely. Alternatively, the teacher can have the children stand up, stretch, jump three times, turn around, and then sit back down. Most children should be ready to refocus again.

All humans can focus and concentrate more efficiently on their work by taking designated breaks throughout the day. Sitting in a stationary position decreases concentration levels and optimal brain activity over time because the blood pools in the legs and backside while oxygen levels decrease. The human body was made to move not sit still. When you get up and move around, you increase blood flow and oxygen levels and help nerve cells to fire properly. Because people of all ages are spending more time on screens, they must take frequent breaks away from the screens for optimal productivity, learning and stress reduction.

Besides taking designated brain wakes or breaks, children and adults can also benefit from more kinesthetic types of furniture. Standing and treadmill desks are available for those who must utilize the computer for much of their jobs. Schools can obtain pieces of kinesthetic classroom furniture to encourage children to move while they work on academic projects traditionally completed at stationary desks. However, this furniture can be expensive and probably is not an option for most schools. Instead, everyone can take designated and purposeful brain breaks/wakes throughout the day. When you purposely take those breaks, your brain and body will work more efficiently. You will be more productive, At the same time, you will prevent many chronic diseases while also decreasing stress.

Action Steps to add more exercise to relieve stress and improve your health:

1. Just get started — Start somewhere at your level and find something you can enjoy or at least tolerate that will get you moving by yourself or with an exercise buddy or trainer. You do not have to start with long aerobic sessions. Walking or stretching for 10-15 minutes several times per day is a great way for beginners to start. Always consult with your doctor if you have not been exercising. Ask them to give you the green light to get moving.

2. Give yourself a break — Take designated brain breaks/wakes at least every 30 minutes throughout the day especially if you work a sedentary job. Give children many opportunities to move throughout the day.

3. Stick it out — Figure out a system that will allow you to succeed long-term. Exercise must be manageable for your lifestyle, at your level, and a priority for you.

4. Be positive — If you stop exercising because you mess up or need to take a break for a health reason, do not beat yourself up. Just start up again when you're able and know you can do it.

L<small>AUGH</small>
E<small>XERCISE</small>
A<small>TTITUDE OF</small> <small>GRATITUDE</small> &
GIVING BACK
R<small>ELAX</small>, R<small>EFLECT</small>, R<small>ECHARGE</small>
N<small>UTRITION</small>

6

IT'S ALL ABOUT YOUR ATTITUDE, BABY!

One of my favorite quotes from Mother Teresa is "Be thankful in the small things; it is in them that your strength lies." This important thought helps me and will hopefully help you keep your head above water. We are at the "A" part of our L.E.A.R.N. acronym.

Is Your Glass Half-Empty or Half-Full?

Living with an attitude of gratitude and giving back is key if you want to live a life with more joy, peace, and less stress! We all know someone in our lives who has that Eeyore personality type who rarely has something positive to talk about. You remember Eeyore from the Winnie the Pooh books and movies. He is the donkey who is always having a bad day. Perhaps you have met a cashier at the grocery store or at a fast-food establishment who has a negative attitude or a chip on his/her shoulder. Recall how that attitude reflected on your customer experience. Recently, I went through the grocery checkout lane and could see the gal at the cash register was not looking particularly happy. I asked her how she was doing.

"I have been better," she replied.

When someone says something like this to me, I usually try and point out something positive. It was a frigid Iowa winter day, but the sun was bright outside.

"But the sunshine sure is nice!" I said.

"Yeah, but it's still cold out," she answered.

"I wish for you to have a better day," I responded.

Sometimes, we need to get the lead out of our "but." This is a catch phrase that Kantis Simmons utilizes in his YouTube video, ***Good Teachers Don't Quit: 5 Ways to Avoid Burnout***.[33] In the video, he teaches educators how to avoid burnout by helping them flip their attitude when stressed. We can all utilize this idea because the "buts" often cause us to focus on the negative things in life instead of looking at the positive. The checkout gal was focused on the "but" instead of her customers and the positive things she could take away during her job.

Now, compare that experience with the customer service I often receive at Chick-fil-A. Each time I go to this fast-food restaurant to order my healthy chicken salad or grilled chicken nuggets and occasionally fries or a shake, their employees greet me positively. They are eager to give me the best experience possible at their establishment. They always answer with, "My pleasure" when I thank them for my order. If the order is wrong, they quickly correct it and apologize. During COVID-19, they were especially helpful and speedy. I always left with a positive feeling because they made me feel important. When I twisted balloons for an event at my local Chick-Fil-A, they gave me free food and treated me with the utmost respect. That sometimes doesn't happen at gigs at other businesses. No wonder they have been named the most beloved fast-food chain in America by the Customer Satisfaction Index's annual restaurant report.[34]

Those who are habitual complainers can suck the joy right out of other people. A quote I recently discovered by an anonymous author may help explain what I am trying to say.

"Stay away from negative people. They have a problem for every solution." When you are around these individuals, it feels like they are backing a large dump truck right into your life as they dump their gloomy garbage straight onto your front lawn. When you ask them how they are doing, they often bring up all the problems in their lives, or they complain about everything. They might even have a permanent scowl on their faces. If you don't know any of these individuals, guess what? You might be lucky, or you might be that person!

Grateful Living

What is gratitude? The root word for gratitude comes from the Latin word gratus. In Pruyser's book, *The Minister as Diagnostician: Personal Problems in Pastoral Perspective*[35] he states, "As to its best name, almost any cognate or derivative of the Latin gratia is worth considering (grace, graciousness, gratitude, gratefulness). They all have something to do with kindness, generosity, gifts, the beauty of giving and receiving, or getting something for nothing."

When we develop this attitude of gratitude, we have a better perspective about life and are more positive and thankful. "Gratitude as a positive emotion, broadens one's perspective and builds other positive emotions or attributes."[36] When we associate with negative people, our sense of gratitude decreases.

I know several people who have the personality types of Debbie Downer, Negative Nancy, or Eeyore. An individual who has done some contract work for us could wear an Eeyore ID around his neck. Each time he comes to our house to work, I ask him how his day is going. Nine times out of ten, he shuffles through the door and explains how terrible he feels. He then details all the negative aspects of his business or problems with family members. Because he does good work, we continue to hire him, but I try not to engage in his negativity. Instead, I try to point out positive things going on that day.

At past work environments, social groups, and family gatherings, I have experienced people who complained and found nothing positive to discuss. It is hard to be around these people as they pop my positivity balloon in a hurry, and I develop a negative attitude as well.

Changing Your Attitude

At one of my teaching jobs, I tried to re-focus my energy and change my attitude about a frustrating situation. I taught at an elementary school and worked with a guy I will call "Frank." Frank did not do his job well. He was one of the custodians in the building. In my opinion, the custodians, secretaries, support and kitchen staff are some of the most important members of any school employee team as they can make or break how the school functions. They contribute positively or negatively to the overall school culture. They often interact with parents, students, staff, and the public while they keep the school running and present either a positive or negative experience for each person who encounters them.

Frank was a nice man and had a big job to do. Unfortunately, he often did not keep things clean, didn't remove snow on the playground before students trampled on it, and didn't supervise the other custodians under his management well. He also had a negative or apathetic attitude. So, I pitched in to help clean or re-clean what Frank or other custodians were supposed to have cleaned. This took me away from my other duties as a physical education teacher. I complained about the situation to other staff members and others. The situation affected my attitude and brought me down. It likely affected others as well. The building's cleanliness issues were brought up numerous times with supervisors over the years. The situation never improved during my time at that school.

I finally decided that I needed to change my attitude because it was affecting the way I interacted with other staff members and with my family. As Albert Einstein said, "Nothing happens until something moves." To put it another way, if nothing changes, nothing changes. Frank was probably not going to change his ways. Thus, if I didn't change my attitude about the situation nothing would ever change for me. So, I pitched in where needed. I praised Frank and other custodians when I noticed them doing a good job. Last, I tried to keep negative comments to myself so that I had more gratitude rather than complaints. It wasn't always easy because this situation was difficult, but when I exhibited a positive attitude, I felt better. Here is something I said to myself when I encountered a place at school that needed recleaning or as I took out the trash in my office. "I get to come to this school and help keep things clean and tidy. I have a job that impacts kids and get to have fun doing it." I struggled some days to keep this positive thought in my mind, but I did my best to keep a positive attitude.

Conversely, I also worked at many schools and other jobs where there were those positive people who made it fun to come to work. Another custodian whom I will call "Roger" was one of the most positive and helpful people at a school where I taught. The kids and staff appreciated his positive attitude and his attention to detail as he kept things cleaned and organized. He was a great storyteller and often made us chuckle during the day. He was a joy to have as the custodian of that school and helped me to focus more on my job of teaching rather than worrying about the cleanliness of the building.

Fake It Till You Make It

How do you react when you run into someone with a bad attitude? If you have ever spent time in a teachers' lounge or company break room, you might have overheard several of these negative individuals. It makes work challenging when people complain a lot. It's human nature to join in on the complaining, retreat, or avoid those individuals all together.

A technique I utilize is to force myself to smile when I am around negative people for an extended period. Do you remember our discussion about the negative effects of elevated levels of cortisol on our brains and bodies in Chapter 3? When we laugh or smile, cortisol is diminished which decreases stress and improves our mood. Even if you do not feel like smiling, walk into the bathroom, look in the mirror, and smile a few times. Additionally, take a few deep breaths after you encounter a negative person or frustrating situation. Find something positive about the challenging or focus on something that went well during the day. When I smile in the mirror for a few moments, I re-focus my attitude from the negative to the positive.

Purposeful Gratitude

When we can focus on gratitude, we achieve a more positive attitude and reduces stress. I do this at least twice a day — during my morning quiet and exercise time and before bedtime. I have found that thanking God for all my many blessings as a part of my Christian faith helps me deal with stress and to experience more joy in my life. If you do not practice a religion, you still will find it helpful to think about things for which you are thankful. That might be as simple as making a list of things you have been given in your life such as:

1. I am alive and well.
2. I have oxygen to breathe.
3. I have a warm house in which to live.
4. I have a family who cares about me.

5. I saw sunshine today.

6. I have a pet who makes me laugh.

Even when I make a conscious effort to be thankful for simple things, I occasionally complain or exhibit a negative attitude. Usually, that is when Paul asks me, "So what are you thankful for today?" That question can annoy me when I am full of self-pity, anger, or frustration. But most of the time that question refocuses my attention back to being gracious or to express my negativity in a more constructive way. Some possible constructive ways to express negativity are exercising, playing music, praying, meditating, giving back to others, or taking time to relax. Chronically negative people probably will not like Paul's question, but you might try asking that question the next time you are around a pessimistic, negative person.

Dr. Chuck Swindoll, author and pastor, has the right insight on the effect of our attitudes. He says, "The longer I live, the more I realize the impact of attitude on life. Attitude, to me, is more important than facts. It is more important than the past, the education, the money, than circumstances, than failure, than successes, than what other people think or say or do. It is more important than appearance, giftedness, or skill. It will make or break a company … a church … a home. The remarkable thing is we have a choice every day regarding the attitude we will embrace for that day." How true! You are the only one who can change your attitude each day.

Another positive person who made a big impact on me in a few minutes was a waiter I encountered at an airport. A few years ago, Paul and I were at a major airport and were looking for a place to eat lunch. We found a restaurant not far from our gate and were waited on by the most fun and positive server I have ever encountered. He was doing his job well and made a stressful situation fun for everyone he encountered. I do not remember the food we ate that day, but that server made a lasting impression with his upbeat attitude!

The next time I was in that same airport, I went back to that restaurant because of my previous experience. He was there again but did not wait on me. However, I observed him, and he impressed me with the way he made his customers feel important. He helped them laugh and didn't let the grumpy travelers get to him. I went over and expressed my appreciation for his excellent customer service and great attitude. I spoke about how he affected me as a customer. He was thankful that I mentioned my gratitude. "Life is too short to be in a bad mood," he responded.

His mindset made all the difference. He was probably not making that much money in an airport restaurant as a server, and I am certain he encountered plenty of stressed and grumpy travelers, but he chose to come to work and do a great job with an even better attitude! His excellent customer service and great outlook made a huge difference for me and many other customers in a short amount of time.

In many circumstances, you cannot control what happens, but you do have a choice in how you react to the situation either positively or negatively. We all know people who have been dealt rough circumstances but choose to look on the bright side. We also know individuals who seem blessed but choose to complain. How do you approach life? Are you a "glass half empty" or "glass half full" kind of person? Here is a list of people who kept a great attitude in the face of adversity. You can search for them online.

- Elisabeth Elliot
- Abby and Brittany Hensel,
- Michelle Knight
- Congressman John Lewis
- Chris Norton
- John O'Leary

- Jackie Robinson
- Amy Van Dyken-Rouen
- Matt Stutzman
- Joni Eareckson Tada
- Nick Vucijic

Despite their hardships, they are or were positive and inspirational people. I know they have had rough, feeling blue days like the rest of us, but they chose to move forward and stay positive. You can do the same! You can choose how to approach life each day and how to react with either a positive or negative attitude.

Happiness Versus Joy

It is easier to be grateful when we are happy, and things are going well. However, happiness is fleeting. Many people are looking for happiness but do not find it because their happiness is based on circumstances. On the other hand, joy is when you find satisfaction regardless of your circumstances. Each year, the World Happiness Report "ranks 156 countries by how happy their citizens perceive themselves to be."[37] Despite the economic blessings many Americans enjoy, people in the USA are not happy. In fact, the United States ranked 18th in the world in the 2020 report.

Scandinavian countries consistently rank high in this report, and Finland has been number one for several years in a row. What does this World Happiness Report use to determine happiness? "The survey, conducted by Gallup, uses a three-year rolling average of survey responses around six factors: Gross Domestic Product (GDP) per capita; social support; life expectancy; freedom to make life choices; generosity; and corruption levels. Finland scores well on all factors but particularly strongly on generosity. The authors say that helping others makes you feel better, but only if you choose to do it. Almost half of Finns donate regularly to charity and almost a third said they had given up time to volunteer for a charity in the previous month."[38]

A few years ago, my brother and his family hosted a high school foreign exchange student from Finland. I asked her whom I will call, "Aino" why she thinks Finland ranks #1 on this report. At first, she said she didn't know why Finland ranked highest. But as she thought about it, she attributed happiness to family connection and the quality of their education system. Aino explained that many of her relatives live in close proximity, and she sees them on a regular basis. Additionally, Finland's education system is very good and includes a free college education.

Regardless of the reasons someone is happy or not, I believe several things contribute to unhappiness in American people. The breakdown of the American family contributes to much of our unhappiness in the United States. The divorce rate is about 50 percent which creates much chaos and unhappiness for families. I know there are viable reasons for divorce, but it has been my observation that many couples do not approach marriage with the intention of making it work long-term even in difficult situations.

Divorce is a challenging process for all involved, especially for children. The dedication and work it takes to create a healthy relationship are key to being happy. If you are in an unhealthy relationship or have gone through a divorce, seek out a good counselor who can help you navigate these stormy waters as you make positive changes.

Distracted with Devices

I have observed that many family members are distracted by devices. Rather than connecting with each other, they spend time on electronic devices. This can lead to loneliness, addiction, financial debt, and time apart from each other. In the World Happiness report, one section charts the usage of digital media by teens since 2006 and its correlation to happiness. As usage increased and face-to-face interaction decreased, the report indicated that happiness rates lowered. "In short, adolescents who spend more time on electronic devices are less happy, and adolescents who spend more time on most other activities are happier. This creates the possibility that iGen adolescents are less happy because their increased time on digital media has displaced time that previous generations spent on non-screen activities linked to happiness."[39] It is my belief that both teens and adults could increase happiness and create more joy in their lives by decreasing their dependence on electronic devices.

Discover ways you and your family can put down the devices and connect, do things together, have quiet time, and reflect on life. Time on digital media robs precious time away from connecting to those closest to you. It also adversely affects your ability to maintain or improve your mental and spiritual health. The COVID-19 lockdown may have helped families take more time to connect because schools and activities were closed and athletic and performing events were cancelled. Families were all together more than any other time in recent history. I believe that families that took time to connect enhanced their relationships and grew closer together. Unfortunately, there were probably just as many families who all sequestered to their devices and failed to take the opportunity to spend time with each other based on surveys in 2020[40]. How did you spend the lockdown or other instances when you had time with those you love? Did the time at home help you grow as an individual and a family?

Commit to Your Peace of Mind

I have committed to starting each day with exercise, prayer, and meditation. I do this before I look at my phone, social media, texts, and email messages. This has improved my attitude. I might utilize a device to listen to a devotional study as I am exercising, but I try not to look at other things or any news until I complete my 30 minutes of morning time.

Some days, I rise at 5:00 am to exercise and have quiet time. I have found that if I don't make time for this, I am less prepared to face the day in a positive way. At the end of the day, I put away my digital devices at least 30 minutes before going to bed. This allows my brain to settle and gives me time to read a book, watch a little TV, and spend time reflecting on the day with Paul. Maybe you can start by putting the devices away for 20 minutes to read a book or take a walk. You must consciously be aware of digital and news media and how they affect your attitude. We will discuss the importance of quiet and reflection in chapter 8.

The Role of Faith in Happiness

Lastly, I believe spiritual faith and wellness can contribute to happiness and joy. However, a 2019 survey revealed the time teens and emerging adults spend on religious activities has declined in recent years. "Millennials are less religious than GenX'ers and Boomers, a result that could have been due to age (perhaps younger people have always been less religious than older people). These analyses instead suggest a cultural change toward less religious involvement."[41] Adults are not much different. According to this survey, over half of American adults seldom or never attend church or synagogue, and only 23 percent attend every week. A Gallup poll reveals that church membership has decreased sharply in the last 20 years. "The decline in church membership is consistent with larger societal trends in declining church attendance and an increasing proportion of Americans with no religious preference."[42]

I believe that people with strong faith are more at peace and have more joy because they have a higher power outside themselves to rely upon and trust. Children who attend church on a regular basis learn teachings on love, respect, kindness, the golden rule. They develop strong positive values that help them to know that they are loved by God. The adults in their lives can also give them love and provide a supportive community. Children develop coping skills during hard times. They can also discover a sense of purpose.

Adults tend to be less self-centered and give more of their time when they have faith. There is a link between religion and helping others according to the article by Christopher Einolf[43] People with religious values motivate prosocial behaviors. And when you focus on others by being kind and giving back, you in turn feel better about yourself and less focused on the trials and negative situations you might be experiencing.

I found personal faith in God as an elementary student. This has helped me navigate through the many trials and blessings in my life. I continue to be active in my faith journey. It has given me a sense of purpose on Earth. Further it has helped me know it's not all about me because I know God is in charge, and I am not. I share joy with other people through one of my gifts and talents God has given me. I cannot imagine finding joy without God.

Action Steps to practice an attitude of gratitude:

1. Remember that you cannot control everything in your life, but you can choose how you react to each situation with a positive or negative response.
2. Practice thankfulness every day at a designated time. Recall the specific things for which you are thankful even if they seem trivial. This might be helpful to do with someone else to help keep you accountable. Focus on the positive things being mindful of the present rather than looking into the past or worrying about what might happen in the future.
3. Hang out with positive people. Notice those people in your life or those strangers that you encounter

    that have a good attitude or are bringing joy to others.

4. If you must be around negative people, limit your time and set good boundaries with them. You are not responsible for anyone else's happiness. You can certainly bring joy to the world, but every person has to be responsible for his/her own attitude.

5. Keep a gratitude journal and frequently look at the things you write down each day to remind you of all your blessings.

6. Limit your exposure to news and social media information that focuses on negative news. You may want to reduce the time you spend on your smartphone and other devices if that time is bringing your attitude down.

7. Demonstrate kindness and giving back to others which will be discussed in the next chapter.

Sally with her therapy dogs Honey and Carly.

7

GIVING BACK

Mister Rogers

"There are three ways to ultimate success. The first way is to be kind. The second way is to be kind. The third way is to be kind. We live in a world in which we need to share responsibility." -Fred Rogers

What great advice from an individual who was one of the kindest and most humble people that lived during my lifetime. I grew up watching Mister Rogers. I have read his biography and watched films about his life. His unique perspective on life and his lifelong career ministering to children through his television program provide a framework from which many of us can learn about giving back to others and learning how to listen and reflect in silence.

We live in a world that is fast-paced and ever-changing with the expectation of instant gratification of selfish desires. Selfishness leads to unhappiness and an unhealthy lifestyle. Thus, I wanted to include giving back to others as a way to stay healthy and reduce stress. According to the Bureau of Labor Statistics, in 2015, about 25 percent of Americans volunteered their time to community, educational, and religious organizations.[44] When individuals give back to others and display kindness toward others, they remove the focus from themselves and their troubles and orient on helping others. This, in turn, can result in emotional and physiological benefits. The chance to give back to others provides the social connection that we desperately need in our digital world.

Why Give Back and Volunteer?

I grew up with the expectation and experience of giving to others because my parents prioritized it. During my youth, I belonged to Girl Scouts, and 4-H. I participated in many activities at school and church and had numerous opportunities to volunteer. My parents were good role models in this practice, and I often observed them giving back to others.

My father gave away vegetables he grew, helped kids in Boy Scouts or 4-H, assisted seniors, and spent time with us kids and our friends. He died when I was 20, but I remember when he invited one of my high school friends to our farm, so she could see a mama sow give birth. (This is a pregnant female pig for those of you who may not know). My friend Diane was so delighted for this opportunity she went on to major in biology, received a master's degree in zoology/animal biology, and eventually got a degree as a nurse practitioner. She worked as an obstetric nurse and is now a certified midwife who helps human moms give birth. My Dad volunteered his time in small ways that made a difference. He would get a kick knowing that when he invited Diane to see the births of those baby piglets, he likely sparked her interest in human obstetrics.

My mother, Kathy, has also always been a helper throughout her life with her own family and others. She has provided meals, sewing, and help with neighborhood children. Even in her retirement, she gives much of her time to help grandchildren and others. She was a foster grandparent for a while. She assisted in a kindergarten room at the elementary school I attended as a youngster. There, she listened to kindergarteners read and do their math which provided a sense of stability for them. Although she has two master's degrees, was a secondary teacher and worked at the university for decades in a variety of professional jobs, she took this role of being foster grandparent in humble stride as an opportunity to give of her time to those in need. In her retirement, she volunteered at a local women's shelter sorting donated clothes and food and also volunteered many hours at several of my schools helping where we needed her.

Now at age 90, her physical abilities and vision have diminished. However, she still wants to help others. I call her the greeting card and flower queen. She loves to send cards and flowers to family members, friends, and others who need a smile or encouragement. She even helped me edit this very book. Best of all she is a good listener which is one of the best ways we can give back to others. I believe all that my mom contributes to others has resulted in her grateful and positive attitude about life.

Sometimes, people do not need you to do anything. They just need you to be quiet, listen, and not try to fix their problems. When you focus your attention on a child or adult, you give them a precious gift that is completely free. It also seems to be less frequent with all the distractions of this world. So many people are focused on their devices rather than on other people. I believe listening is one of the best ways you can give back to those you love and even to strangers. How might you stop and listen to someone today? Everyone has a story to tell if we take the time to listen.

There are many individuals and families who are great listeners, give of their time, talents and money to volunteer. They give back to their communities which makes the world a better place. During the COVID-19 pandemic, many people gave back and are still giving back to their neighbors, communities, and the world. Countless individuals volunteered at food banks, shopped, or delivered food for those who were not able to go out, and showed kindness in other ways.

How I Give Back

I began giving back when I was young and still volunteer my time. I do this for various organizations, at church, or on my own. One of my most rewarding volunteer endeavors is when I take my therapy dogs out into the community at least once a month. Although, COVID curtailed this activity. I take them to senior centers or nursing homes, to the local university for college students to de-stress. I also share them with children at schools or in church. Dog training is something I started doing as a young 4-H member and have enjoyed training, showing, and sharing my dogs with others. One of my dogs performed in my Silly Sally shows as she loved children.

The human-animal bond is extraordinarily strong. People of all ages relate to a dog through petting it and making that emotional connection. For 25 years, I was one of our local volunteer 4-H dog project leaders. I taught young people about dog training and general dog care. I still judge youth dog shows and other 4-H exhibits at many county fairs and at the Iowa State Fair.

I believe strongly in the 4-H program because it gives youth opportunities to learn and practice life skills such as public speaking, setting goals, leadership, volunteering their time, teamwork with their club members and working through project challenges as they complete a fair exhibit.

I also volunteered many years for the American Red Cross. I taught first aid and CPR classes at our local chapter to thousands in my community and at businesses. I still volunteer at the American Heart Association for our school fundraiser. Both volunteer endeavors are in honor of my dad whose passing was the result of a sudden heart attack.

My husband Paul and I enjoy sharing our music together at church and at local nursing homes. Like petting a dog, music can help a person make an emotional connection and bring back memories. Seniors enjoy singing along to the songs we share. This brings as much joy to us as it does to the recipients. Numerous times, I have observed seniors who might not otherwise interact with others join in singing songs with us. I also volunteer my time to entertain people of all ages as Silly Sally. Before COVID, I began mentoring a young girl at one of our local schools. This gave me a different experience and perspective than when I am teaching an entire class. It was a way I could give back to a child in my community who needed a positive adult role model.

I shared about my volunteer experiences to illustrate how volunteering gives me a sense of joy while it also makes a positive difference in the world. I get as much out of giving to others as the recipients receive from me. I can shine God's light to others and volunteering gets me out of my own troubles and re-focuses my attention on others. If I am having a bad day and take time to do something for others, it gets me out of my funk and keeps me from focusing on my troubles at least for a little while. An anonymous quote I like about giving is, "The meaning of life is to find your gift. The purpose of life is to give it away."

Random Acts of Kindness Make a Difference

You have something to share with others regardless of your skills and talents. Maybe you can do random acts of kindness. Have you ever tried paying for someone's order at the drive through? Helped at a homeless shelter? Sent flowers anonymously to someone to cheer them up? Put money in expired parking meters? These small acts of kindness can be impactful for you and the recipient.

Here are the random acts of kindness I have performed. A few years ago, Paul and I were walking through downtown

Denver where there were several homeless people. We came across a couple of men and started talking to them. We discovered they were veterans, and we offered to buy them some sandwiches. They agreed, so we went to a local fast-food sandwich shop and ordered them food. They were thankful for our small act of kindness.

Another time, we helped a homeless person after we had eaten at a wonderful famous BBQ restaurant in Kansas City. We had more food than we could eat. We decided to box up our meal anyway as we saw some guys who were homeless outside the restaurant area. We figured we would give them our leftovers. However, when we went back outside to give them the food, they were gone. We continued to look for someone else on our way back to the car but had no luck. Once we were back in the car, we prayed and asked God to show us someone who would enjoy our leftovers. We drove for quite a while and were about to give up when we saw a man standing near an intersection under a bridge. We pulled over and asked him if he would like our meal. He enthusiastically took our famous BBQ meal and ran off the road as he thanked us. God knew he needed that meal, and we were in the right place at the right time.

I know that I cannot fix all the homeless problems, and there are likely people who may take advantage of my generosity. I try and help where I can and let God take care of the rest. If someone is lying about their need or taking advantage of my help, I cannot control that behavior, and it is between them and God.

I am careful and diligent where I give cash, items, gifts, or time, but it is not for me to judge others and their situations. If I become aware that someone took advantage of my help, I set a boundary and give them no further opportunities to take advantage of me.

Another way I help is that I keep $5 fast food gift cards in my car so when I see someone asking for help, I can hand them a card they can utilize for a meal. I don't give cash and started giving out gift cards when I was with a friend in Las Vegas for a conference. There were so many homeless people asking for help, that we purchased gift cards and gave them out.

Paul, my mom, and I have made meals for the emergency residence shelter in our town. The meals were not the most important part of the work. Rather, we stayed and ate with the men. We listened to them, and that was how we gave back to those less fortunate than us.

Maybe you do not have a lot of extra time, but if you have been blessed financially, you can always make a cash contribution or provide groceries at your local food pantry. Everyone can do something. "All of us, at some time or other, need help. Whether we're giving or receiving help, each one of us has something valuable to bring to this world. That's one of the things that connects us as neighbors — in our own way, each one of us is a giver and receiver."[45]

Even during difficult times, we can find ways to give back. For example, during COVID-19, I did random acts of kindness. I took meals to the seniors in my family and found other ways to help people. Giving back during the pandemic meant I had to do things differently, but I was still able to help.

It's Okay to Ask for Help

Maybe you are reading this and need help yourself. It is hard to ask for help especially if you have been an independent person and have given back to others. Remember that when someone offers you help, you give them an opportunity to give back. It is a gift for them to be able to help you. It is not a sign of weakness when you need help. Rather, it is a way to help others give you a gift of their time. Many of us feel that by asking for help or accepting help from others, we are inconveniencing the person or being a burden. Author Courtney Westlake explains, "Letting others help you when you are in need allows God to weave through both of you, connecting you and humbling your hearts. Accepting help is actually giving others the gift of being able to take action and show love to you when they might otherwise feel helpless."[46]

We all need help at times in our lives. Asking for help does not mean you are a failure or are weak but allows other people to be blessed through their acts of kindness and service. When we go through those valleys in our lives, we need to stay connected to others. Isolating can lead to depression and sink your boat. Allowing others to help gives you opportunities to be in contact with people and build supportive relationships which is important in those times of need. Good friends and family can listen and help you process difficulties and give helpful insights.

It is also important to de-stress and process whatever difficulty you may be facing. After 9/11, a retired Mister Rogers went back on Public Broadcasting System (PBS) to encourage viewers to look for the helpers. He related a story he had told many times before, but it was especially important at that time. "When I was a little boy and something bad happened in the news, my Mother would tell me to look for the helpers. 'You'll always find people helping,' she'd say. And I've found that that's true. In fact, it's one of the best things about our wonderful world."[47] There are people out there who are your helpers. You might just need to look for them and ask for help.

As Mister Rogers said, it is okay to ask for help. Conversely, those who help us also reap benefits. Thus, this exchange can be mutually beneficial. Keeping a positive attitude and giving back to others or asking for help are life savers. As you travel on the waves of life, remember that you have the power to choose your attitude and how you react to every situation. "If you don't like something, change it. If you can't change it, change your attitude." -Maya Angelou

Action Steps in giving back to others:

1. Find at least one way you can volunteer and help someone else. This might be working with a nonprofit organization, church, or philanthropic organization you believe in, or it could be calling a friend or neighbor who lives alone and needs someone to listen to them.
2. Try to do a random act of kindness this week. Here are some simple ideas. Put money in someone else's parking meter. Pay for the order of the car behind you in the fast-food drive through line. Say hello, ask some questions and take interest in a neighbor you do not know. Take some food to someone in need. Leave a larger tip for a server at a restaurant. Send flowers to someone for no special occasion. Send someone a card in the mail. Tell the cashier or convenience store worker how much you appreciate their efforts at work.
3. Think of someone who needs a listening ear and call, visit, or have a meal together while utilizing your active listening skills to demonstrate kindness, care, and concern.

Laugh
Exercise
Attitude of Gratitude &
Giving Back
Relax, Reflect, Recharge
Nutrition

8

RELAX, REFLECT, AND RECHARGE

In this chapter we will be moving on to the "R" in the L.E.A.R.N. acronym. This includes the three R's: Relax, Reflect and Recharge. I want to discuss the importance of relaxation and quiet reflection in recharging your mind, body and spirit.

Of all the L.E.A.R.N. principles, relaxation is the hardest one for me. I admit that I am not good at stopping to relax and taking time to just chill, and I need to improve. My husband often reminds me of this, and I am working on it. I need to remember that rest is not a "four letter word."

In my own faith, I often turn to the Bible for instruction. It tells me that God created the universe in six days, and on the seventh day He rested. Many other religions also encourage meditation, deep breathing, reflection, and prayer. Yoga began in India as a Hindu practice. Its original purpose rooted in self-awareness and training of the body and mind. Yoga utilizes deep breathing along with body poses to practice meditation to balance mind, body, and spirit. The Dalai Lama, a Buddhist monk, practices a daily regimen of prayer and meditation and has linked that practice to being a more positive person. Silence and reflection are also practiced and encouraged in the Islamic faith. Whether or not you practice a particular faith, you will benefit your mind and body if you take time to relax, reflect, and recharge.

Importance of Relaxation

I like this quote from Mark Black, "Sometimes the most productive thing you can do is relax." We need to recharge and let our bodies rest to be at our most productive. I am more productive when I take scheduled breaks to relax during the week or weekend. I take time on Sunday for rest and relaxation and almost always attend church worship services. Things come up for me and some weekends I end up at a gig and don't take designated down time. When this happens, I am more edgy, stressed and tired. I know I must take time to relax, but this is a hard one for me. The COVID-19 lockdown forced me to stay home and not work as much which led to a much-needed break to recharge and refresh.

Be Quiet

Along with relaxation, we need to be quiet and reflect on our life each day. In 1994, Mister Rogers talked about the importance of taking time to be quiet and to reflect. "I'm very concerned that society is much more interested in information than wonder, in noise rather than silence. How do we encourage reflection? Oh, my this is a noisy world."[48] We do live in a noisy world. Imagine what Mister Rogers might think now with the prevalence of so many distracting devices to occupy everyone's time and minds.

Many people have a difficult time being with themselves in silence. Because I am an introvert and lived by myself for many years before I was married, I think this comes easier for me than for those who are more extroverted. I actually enjoyed the first couple of months of COVID-19 and the lockdown. I value solitude and quiet time to reflect each day. When I spend a day at school teaching with all the noise and busyness, I usually collapse at the end of the day. I need quiet time to recharge before I am ready to do anything else. I can create music, words on a page, videos or my many programs and shows when I am alone in silence. COVID-19 gave me time to reflect and create which I appreciated.

I, too, get caught up in the noise and distractions. Sometimes, I forget to stop and be quiet without the interference of screens, work, and family. My morning time of 30 minutes each day to exercise, pray, and reflect has improved my physical and mental well-being. It is easy for my mind to wander and focus on negative thoughts. Therefore, I commit to prayer and reflection, so I stay on track. Each morning, I consciously go through a process as I pray and reflect, so I stay on-track. If I do not intentionally do this, my mind wanders and focuses on negative things or tasks that need to be done. Then, I experience more stress.

Another technique that may help you when you are working to reduce stress is to practice mindfulness. To practice mindfulness, concentrate on what you are feeling and sensing in the present moment. My ACT acronym will help you stay focused while you are in your quiet reflection time.

Acknowledge

Concentrate

Take Action

Acknowledge how you feel. What do you notice about yourself and your surroundings? Are you stressed, calm, angry, happy, or sad? Where are you in terms of your feelings and focus? Try not to think about the future or any regrets from the past. Instead, acknowledge your present state of mind and your surroundings.

The **C** stands for concentrate. After you acknowledge your feelings and the things going on around you, concentrate on your breathing. Breathwork will calm your body and give you a sense of peacefulness. You might want to utilize the 4-7-8 method of breathing. To do this, inhale for four seconds, hold your breath for seven seconds, and then slowly exhale for eight seconds.

Another way you can concentrate on your breathing is to put your hands on your abdomen and say to yourself, "Breathe in and breathe out" while you perform slow deep breaths. It is important for you to take deep cleansing breaths as this helps your body get full oxygen exchange. Your exhalation of carbon dioxide can help slow your heartrate, lower blood pressure, and decrease your stress level. I find one of these techniques helpful when I am in the midst of a stressful situation, or when I have insomnia.

Finally, Take Action! This means you will move forward in the ways you can control. You can review any action steps or goals you are working toward and/or visualize yourself being successful in your wellness journey.

As I discussed Chapter 6, often you cannot control what happens to you, but you can control your attitude and how you react to a situation. This is important as you take action in reducing your stress while you use the ACT process. Review your goals as you visualize being successful in improving your health. Try to reduce negative self-talk and concentrate on the steps to help you be successful.

The Importance of Mindfulness

When I was a high school head girls basketball coach, I often utilized visualization and mindfulness techniques with the players after practice or before a game. I helped the players take action with the way they thought about being successful as a basketball team. This sports psychology mental preparation technique was a critical part of our practices and game preparation. It was as crucial as practicing the fundamentals and offensive and defensive plays. This introspective time helped us reflect on the things we were doing well and ways we could improve our skills. It also helped us appreciate each other and helped us concentrate and stay calm before a game.

We started each session by performing breathing techniques while listening to music. We concentrated on the things the team and individual players had done well in practice. We also visualized specific things they could control. Then, they thought about how they could take action on the things they could control in the upcoming game which did not include how the referees made their calls.

You too can use this method to assist you in reducing your stress and improving your health and wellness. I encourage you to try. If you need guidance, many videos online can walk you through a mindfulness session including the videos on my YouTube and website.

Here are some other options to find quiet time. You can take a drive down a country road with the radio off. Sit on your front porch with a cold drink. Take a nature walk away from distractions with your phone in silent mode. Read a book and reflect on its content. Listen to calming music. The above techniques will aid you on your journey to reflect and recharge.

Life at Silly Acres

While in the process of writing this book, we moved out of town into the country. I have always been a country girl at heart and longed for the chance to be back in the countryside. I had to convince my city man that it was a good idea while trying to find a place to purchase within our budget. God blessed us with our acreage property, and we both love all the opportunities for silence without traffic, trains, and other people. We appreciate nature and are observing the gorgeous seasonal sunrises and sunsets over the Iowa countryside. We both enjoy being outside, and I love growing things around our house. We have named our property "Silly Acres" and hope to have many laughs out here where we can watch laughter grow and invite others to enjoy the silence. Hopefully, you have a place where you can put down your devices and be quiet, relax, recharge and reflect about your life.

Put Down Your Phone

It's okay not to respond to your phone calls and texts immediately so you can be quiet for a time. In fact, taking time away from devices and news is healthy. How can you quiet your mind each day to be present with those you love? Can you put your phone down for an hour without constantly checking texts and other notifications?

I have observed parents on their smart phones at restaurants while their children long for their attention or conversation. I have seen families with teens all using their devices instead of talking with each other. We are losing those face-to-face connections as each generation of smart phones and tablets develops more ways to occupy our time. We must be aware of how easily these devices can distract us away from talking to each other. "Technology has given us an unlimited ticket to escape — and our meandering even looks legitimate since so much work is done online."[49] Many young people lack the skills to converse face-to-face or over the phone. This used to be a basic social skill that teens negotiated with ease and pleasure when they socialized. Now, many teens and millennials text and don't talk. They play video games online or on their gaming systems in a virtual world instead of doing an actual activity together in the real world. People of all ages are checking out on devices instead of tuning in to their own lives and feelings. It is my belief that we must consciously put the devices away for designated periods of time and be quiet to relieve stress and recharge.

The Importance of Reflection

Another conscious thing that Paul and I do every evening is to reflect and pray. Each evening before bedtime we review our day together. This has strengthened our marriage over the years. We share our concerns, praises, lows, and highs. We then read a short devotional together and pray before sleep. This quiet time at the end of the day allows me to hush my mind, trust in God, and connect with my husband. Some days, it is difficult as we might be busy into the evening hours or tired, but we try to make it a priority.

For you, it might be that you reflect on your day while you eat with your family. In my opinion, having meals together is crucial for family relationship growth. Conversing over a meal offers families a chance to connect intimately about how life is going. I believe this is an important thing parents can do with their children. They can turn off devices and have face-to-face conversations. Unfortunately, I have observed that many families are not eating together anymore.

I fondly remember that my mother made family mealtime a priority. It became harder when we were all teenagers with our many activities, but we tried to make it work several times a week. My father died when I was 20, and I have missed so many meals with him since his death. Therefore, I am grateful for those family meals we had together when I was growing up. Sometimes, those meals were stressful and felt rushed, but we still sat down at the kitchen table to eat as a family while my parents asked us questions, and we shared about our lives.

Importance of Sleep

Are you sleep deprived? A crucial way to keep our heads above water is through getting adequate sleep. Sleep is an obvious way to relax and be quiet and is important for overall wellness. Sleep deprivation is a problem for many people and can contribute to many health issues such as heart disease, obesity, diabetes, and an overall shorter lifespan.[50] When we get insufficient sleep, it is like riding the waves without a surfboard. Sleep is vital for our brains and bodies. Becutti and Pannain[51] reviewed research correlating sleep deprivation with obesity and stated, "This obesity epidemic has been paralleled by a trend of reduced sleep duration. Poor sleep quality, which leads to overall sleep loss has also become a frequent complaint. Growing evidence from both laboratory and epidemiological studies points to short sleep duration and poor sleep quality as new risk factors for the development of obesity." In a study[52] in 2004, researchers studied the effect of sleep on Body Mass Index (BMI) with over 900 staff participants at several hospitals. They discovered that those staff that got less than six hours of sleep per night did have a higher BMI rate which is consistent with other studies. "Our finding that short sleep duration was associated with increased BMI is consistent with these other studies of adult and childhood populations."

We tend to think better and be more productive when we get a good night of sleep. Most adults need seven to eight hours, but many people sleep far less than that each night.[53] Sleep deprivation drains your brain's ability to focus and think creatively.[54] When we get quality and adequate sleep, our brains can process memory and information which is needed for optimal health. If we don't get adequate and quality sleep, we become irritable which can affect our health and our relationships with others.

Most adults know that sleep is important to function optimally, yet many do not make sleep a priority. We all go through seasons in life when sleep is hard to find, but some people never get enough sleep. According to the CDC website[55], 28 to 44 percent of adults in the United States have sleeping issues with the higher rates in the southeastern states. A vast number of sleep disorders make sleep difficult for many adults. We have way too many sleeping aids to count, but many people still have trouble getting enough sleep. Worry and anxiety also rob many of precious sleep and rest. Some adults choose not to prioritize sleep and fall victim to bad habits that can lead into chronic sleep disorders.

I need a lot of sleep. As I get older, some nights I am prone to insomnia. So, I sympathize with people who have chronic insomnia or a sleep disorder. The following are some ideas that work for me to get the best night's rest and are recommended for good sleep hygiene.[56]

1. Try to be exposed to natural light early in the morning which helps to regulate the circadian rhythm.
2. Create a relaxing sleep environment.
3. Exercise on a regular basis. This is connected to better sleep.
4. Minimize long naps during daytime hours — short cat naps or an afternoon siesta that are of 30 minutes or less can be beneficial.
5. Keep a consistent sleep schedule. Go to bed and wake up at the same time.
6. Before bed, turn the temperature in the room down to 60-68 degrees Fahrenheit.
7. Finish eating at least two to four hours before bedtime.
8. Limit pre-bedtime alcohol and caffeine consumption.
9. Turn off blue light screens at least 30 minutes before falling asleep.
10. If you wake up for more than 20-30 minutes during the night, read a book, pray, meditate with deep

breathing or think about things for which you are grateful. This may help to reset your mind if you are worrying or thinking about something for long periods of time.

11. For longer periods of insomnia, it might be helpful to get up and do a task.
12. Try deep breathing techniques.
13. See a sleep specialist for chronic insomnia issues.

Take Time for the 3 R's

Overall, taking designated time in our schedules to rest and relax is essential for optimal health.[57] Our bodies and brains need time to be quiet, reflect, recharge, and relax. If we don't prioritize them, those sharks looming in the water will take a huge bite of our emotional and physical wellness. Unlike many countries, in America work and busyness is often valued over down time for rest and renewal. We need to take a step back and prioritize what is most important in our lives. For me, faith, family, and my health take precedence over other things.

We need a reminder of just how quickly we can get focused on the wrong things. In 1963, German writer, Heinrich Boll wrote a parable about a fisherman that has been changed slightly over the years, and I have adapted it for the end of this chapter as we think about rest, relaxation and recharging.

An American investment banker was on vacation in a small Mexican coastal town, and he wandered out to a boat pier where several fishermen had their boats docked. The investment banker complimented one of the fishermen on the quality of the large tuna fish he had just caught and asked how long it took to catch them.

"It didn't take long" the fisherman replied.

The American asked the fisherman why he didn't stay out longer to catch more fish.

"These fish will supply the needs for my family today," the fisherman answered.

"But what do you do with the rest of your time?" The banker asked.

"I sleep late, fish a little, play with my children, take a siesta with my wife, stroll into the village each evening where I drink beer and tequila and play guitar with my amigos. I have a full and happy life," the fisherman said.

"Well, I have an MBA (Master of Business Administration) and could help you make your life better. You should spend more time fishing to catch more fish to make more money so that you can buy a bigger boat. Then with the profits from all those fish, you could purchase more boats and hire other guys to fish for you. And eventually buy a whole fleet of fishing boats with more employees. Instead of selling your fish to a middleman, you could sell directly to the processor and eventually you could open up your very own cannery. That way, you would control the product, processing, and distribution. But you would need to leave this small Mexican town and relocate to Mexico City and maybe even to America to run your expanding enterprise," the banker said.

"But how long would that take?" The fisherman asked.

"Fifteen to twenty years."

"But then what?" The fisherman asked.

The investment banker laughed and said, "This is the best part. When the time is right, you would sell your company and make millions."

"What would I do with millions?" asked the fisherman.

"Then you would retire, move to a small coastal fishing village where you could sleep late, fish a little, play with your grandkids, take a siesta with your wife, stroll to the village in the evening, drink beer and tequila while playing guitar with

your amigos. You would have a happy and full retirement and not have to worry about anything," the banker said.

Maybe this story is a wake-up call for you. Are you taking time each day to stop and relax, reflect, and recharge your busy life? Few of us can be like the fisherman in the story and catch enough fish each day to keep us afloat financially. Regardless, we can try to find balance each day so that we enjoy life even in the midst of our work.

Action steps to Relax, Reflect and Recharge:

1. Realize you need to stop and take downtime each week to recharge your mind and body as an important part of stress management. Start with 10 minutes and expand this time as you gain more practice and reap the benefits in quiet and reflection time.

2. Be intentional on how you practice relaxation. Find a technique that works for you. This might include an idea from this book or another way in which you can relax.

3. Put down your devices and distractions for a designated time each day. Learn to embrace quiet time and be mindful of your thoughts and feelings.

4. Make sleep a priority and practice good sleep hygiene. This is one of the best ways to restore your brain and body toward optimal wellness.

LAUGH
EXERCISE
ATTITUDE OF GRATITUDE &
GIVING BACK
RELAX, REFLECT, RECHARGE
NUTRITION

9

FISHING FOR FOOD AND FUELING YOUR BODY

"Seize the moment. Remember all those women on the Titanic who waved off the dessert plate." Erma Bombeck

Food is Medicine

We need to seize the moments in life and not focus too much on the sinking Titanic diet. Instead, we can discover the nutrition that will sustain us for the long haul and could help us reduce stress and bolster our immune system.

In the last chapter, we explored the need for rest and relaxation to stay ahead of the sharks. We need to fish for foods that will nourish and help us stay in the boat. This chapter will take us on our last boat trip as we discuss the "N" which stands for nutrition in our L.E.A.R.N. acronym.

Eating nutritiously can be one of your best anchors as you go on your wellness journey. Food can be medicine. The famous Greek physician Hypocrites may have had the best advice about nutrition, "Let **food** be thy **medicine**, and let **medicine** be thy **food**." The food you eat can work like medicine, or it can work like poison.[58] You can eat robust, nutritious meals that will aid in the prevention of disease and promote care of your body, or you can consume junky, processed foods that can literally make you sick. Not eating the right foods, eating junk food, consuming foods that contain an overabundance of preservatives or overeating can sink your boat as quickly as the iceberg that took down the Titanic.

According to Merriam-Webster[59], nutrition or more specifically the word nourish can be defined as, "to promote growth, to furnish or sustain with nutriment." MedicineNet[60] defines nutrition as, "The process of taking in food and using it for growth, metabolism, and repair."

Are you fueling your body with nutrition that will help you grow and stay healthy? We need to eat to maintain a healthy lifestyle. Finding the appropriate foods that provide the best nourishment can be confusing. This confusion and debate as to what we should be eating causes many people to abandon their nutrition boats and swim for the sharks. In the United States, the abundance and choices of food as well as information about what we should be eating overwhelms most of us. Data from the National Health and Nutrition Examination Survey[61] listed on the Centers for Disease Control website revealed that almost half of American adults tried to lose weight between 2013-2016. We spend billions of dollars on weight loss products every year.

Most people who struggle with food realize they have an issue and recognize the need for change. However, this is one of the hardest things to do and maintain over a lifetime. I admit that if I am not careful and intentional, the chocolate and potato chip gods can lure me into running my boat into some huge icebergs. Each day I must be intentional about what foods I put into my mouth. I strive to eat foods that will fuel me toward a healthy, active lifestyle.

It is not easy, and I can get pulled under when certain situations and foods tempt me. As we age, the challenge increases of staying in a healthy weight range. The good news for me is that most days I do stay on-track, and when I do get pulled under briefly, I am generally able to get back on course quickly. It is a hard task, and I am the first to admit I can anchor my boat right by the ice cream aisle of the grocery store. I pull in that catch and consume the entire box in a few days if I am not mindful of my choices.

It is important to note that it is okay to occasionally indulge in small quantities of food that would be considered unhealthy. This might be helpful for long-term weight management for those individuals because they know it is all right to eat small portions of their favorite foods occasionally. There are also people who may have difficulty eating just a small portion of certain foods. They might realize that indulging in that favorite treat could trigger an entire junk food binge.

You must know your food triggers and how you react to them. If you cannot eat a small number of potato chips and put the bag away, then it is probably best to leave the bag of chips at the grocery store and not have them in your house. I have this issue with ice cream. If ice cream is in my house, I will consume it. So, it is best for me not to have large quantities of ice cream in my freezer, and I only purchase it once in a while as a special treat. When I do purchase it, I try to find brands that have very few ingredients without all the preservatives and preferably from a local dairy. Better yet, I make homemade ice cream, where I control what goes into the recipe.

While quarantined at home during the COVID-19 pandemic, the refrigerator door was more tempting as I spent more time near my kitchen. Some people have joked that many gained the COVID 19 (pounds), as we spent more time at home and less time out doing our "normal" activities outside of the walls of our homes. Many individuals experienced stress and emotional distress during the pandemic which resulted in emotional stress eating. People consume sugar and carb comfort foods when they eat for emotional comfort rather than seeking out healthy alternatives.

The Role of Food in Well-Being and Illness

There is more evidence now than ever before that the foods we consume have an impact on how our bodies perform and feel. Dr. Amy Myers is a functional medicine expert and a strong proponent of the notion that food contributes to our well-being and in healing the body of many autoimmune ailments. Many of these diseases may include aches and pains in the joints and muscles or other chronic pain that could be misdiagnosed as something else. Functional medicine seeks to find the root causes of illness. Doctors collaborate with patients to develop a more individualized approach to medicine and treat the person rather than the symptoms. On the other hand, conventional medicine identifies the symptoms to detect an illness and develop a treatment plan. That often involves the use of pharmaceuticals to lessen the symptoms.

Food allergies and autoimmune diseases are a huge issue for many people. Dr. Myers and many other functional medicine experts believe these diseases can be diminished in part through eliminating some foods while eating healthy foods along with several other lifestyle changes, natural remedies, decreasing stress and diminishing exposure to toxins. I recommend her book, ***The Autoimmune Solution: Prevent and Reverse the Full Spectrum of Inflammatory Symptoms and Diseases***[62] if you want to learn more about the "Myers Way" of treating autoimmune diseases.

Autoimmune diseases can cause low or over activity of the immune system. In response to the cause, the body attacks its own tissues. Autoimmune diseases tend to result in inflammation in the body because inflammation is a normal reaction to tissue damage and pathogen infection. Examples of some common autoimmune diseases are Rheumatoid Arthritis, Type 1 Diabetes, Multiple Sclerosis, Lupus, Grave's disease, Addison's disease, Celiac Disease, Psoriasis/Psoriatic Arthritis, Inflammatory Bowel Disease, Fibromyalgia, Endometriosis and many more.

Pain is often a symptom of inflammation and many foods you eat can increase inflammation in your body even if you do not have an autoimmune disease. If you suffer from undiagnosed pains or have an autoimmune disease, you might want to keep a food journal to determine if certain foods trigger your pain and/or symptoms. A good place to start is to eliminate foods that you suspect might be causing symptoms while you record those foods in a journal. You can slowly reintroduce those foods back into your diet to determine if your symptoms return. It is amazing to me the role that food can play in our wellness or illness, yet so few conventional medicine physicians are knowledgeable about the importance of nutrition in addressing many diseases.

About eight years ago, I was diagnosed with Celiac disease which means I am allergic to gluten (a protein found in wheat, barley, and rye). I believe I had this issue for many years before I was finally diagnosed because Celiac disease often disguises itself with many other problems. Other autoimmune diseases that may not be directly related to the symptoms presented also seem to disguise themselves. Celiac affects the small intestine when gluten is ingested. The body's negative response to gluten leads to damage of the villi that line the small intestine, and therefore the body does not absorb nutrients properly. Other symptoms such as joint pain, fatigue, insomnia, digestive issues including bloating or belching, or other body pains may occur.

I was misdiagnosed for many years with acid reflux which never presented with heart burn, and the doctors prescribed antacids. I had vocal issues and some unexplained pains for over 20 years. My conventional physicians were treating the symptoms and did not seek out the root cause of my issues which were related to the wheat I was ingesting.

I got frustrated at being prescribed medication to treat my symptoms as I was sure there was a reason why I had these issues. I went to a digestive specialist who determined the root cause (gluten) of my symptoms. Since I received the correct diagnosis, I have kept my Celiac in check and feel much better by avoiding gluten.

My take-away lesson from this experience is to know when your body is not functioning properly and be persistent in getting answers from the medical community. It took many years and numerous doctors to figure out what was going on with me. Had I just sat back and not asked questions and persistently pursued an underlying cause for my symptoms, I would still be on antacids and eating foods that were damaging my body. Gluten intolerance and Celiac disease have been on the rise in the last 20 years which may be partially due to more awareness of this condition or changes in the way and what we eat. About one in one hundred adults lives with Celiac disease, but many more have gluten intolerance. The best way to determine if you might have a gluten intolerance is to stop eating foods with gluten and see if you feel better. Many people, including Dr. Myers, advocate for a completely grain-free diet which is extreme but can be helpful for some individuals.

Many people deal with other food intolerances. My sister Mary self-identified that she had a histamine intolerance with classic symptoms that were confirmed by her pulmonologist. She suddenly became extremely ill with an inflammatory issue in her lungs. It affected her overall health and was misdiagnosed by 10 different doctors. They placed her on 13 different medications and breathing treatments every four to six hours in an effort to treat what the doctors thought was uncontrolled asthma. Because Mary is a nurse and pored over the results of many tests, she was not convinced that she had asthma.

She said, "I'm going to figure this thing out because obviously the doctors couldn't figure out exactly what I had, and I didn't believe I had asthma especially when I had a pulmonary function test of 110 to 120 percent and had exercised my entire life without asthma-like symptoms. I started to look at food. Could food be making me sick? I came across high histamine foods. After looking at two Michigan conventionally trained doctors' website information on histamine intolerance and the symptoms, I had all the classic signs related to this condition." Mary started an organic low-histamine, anti-inflammatory, high plant-based and antioxidant diet. In addition, she eliminated processed foods and any foods with potential preservatives, or additives, or chemicals and her symptoms improved. She was able to discontinue 12 of the 13 medications she was previously prescribed and currently has no health limitations. Mary healed herself by controlling the symptoms and reducing the overwhelming systemic inflammation in her body. Her quality of life dramatically improved, and the possibility of becoming disabled disappeared. High histamine foods include those that are fermented like sauerkraut and other pickled foods, nuts, cheese, yogurt, Kefir, certain kinds of fruits and vegetables and many more.

You may not have a food intolerance issue like Mary, or I do, but if you're eating a lot of processed foods, fast food and foods high in sugar and salt, your health is likely compromised or will be in the future. That old saying, "You are what you eat" is true. When you feed your body with fresh fruits, vegetables, and other nutritious foods, you will feel better, and your brain will function with more clarity. In fact, your body will start craving those foods, and you will feel and look better.

Making healthy eating choices is one of the best ways to keep your head above water. It is not easy, but each day you choose what you feed your body. Many fruits and vegetables are filled with age-defying antioxidants, vitamins, nutrients, and fiber that aids digestion. Daily consumption of fruits and vegetables affects how your skin looks, your brain thinks, and your body feels.

Healthy foods may also be linked to a reduction in cardiovascular disease and cancer. A 14-year longitudinal study[63] done as a part of the Harvard-based Nurses' Health Study and Health Professionals followed fruit and vegetable consumption for 110,000 men and women from 1984-1998 to determine risk of major chronic diseases. Results suggest that high consumption of fruits and vegetables, especially green leafy vegetables are associated with a small reduction of risk of major chronic disease. Cardiovascular disease can be diminished by consuming five or more fruits and vegetables daily. Although green leafy vegetables such as lettuce, spinach, chard, and mustard greens were most strongly associated with a decreased prevalence of cardiovascular disease, other vegetables and fruits also contributed to the reduction of cardiovascular disease and some cancers.

Plant Based Diets

For decades, Dr. Dean Ornish has advocated for more of a plant-based diet rather than a traditional American animal-protein-based diet to reduce or reverse many chronic diseases including cardiovascular disease and cancer. In his book, *UnDo It!*[64], he asserts that his eating plan along with exercise, stress reduction, and building relationships can contribute to the reversal of the progressions of many chronic diseases. The Ornish diet includes consuming mostly plant-based foods, minimizing or eliminating animal protein, avoiding sugar, white flour, white rice and other bad carbs, consuming three grams of good omega-3 fatty acids and reducing the intake of total fat especially trans fats, saturated fats, and hydrogenated fats.

I believe this diet will reduce your chances of developing a chronic disease, I also know that it is a challenging plan for most people to maintain long-term. Perhaps, you start with eating five fruits and vegetables, eliminate processed foods, and slowly reduce animal protein or at least red meat. Because I grew up the daughter of an Iowa hog farmer and showed pigs at the fair, I like my Iowa pork chops which can be very lean. I know I need to do better in reducing my meat consumption, but this is a challenge for me. I will keep working on it by eating more poultry and fish, but honestly, I am not sure I could ever go to an all plant-based diet. I have increased my vegetable consumption since being diagnosed with Celiac disease, and my body is now used to having all that fiber and nutrients. I actually miss my veggies if I don't get enough of them on a daily basis.

Organic Food

Many people advocate eating only organic foods and avoiding Genetically Modified Organisms (GMO) foods. You may opt to purchase organic fruits, vegetables, and other organic foods to reduce ingestion of pesticides and GMO foods, but many families cannot afford to eat organic foods. If you do not have access to or cannot afford organic foods, you have other options.

An excellent option in a temperate climate is to grow your own food. I have a small garden with vegetables, raspberries, blueberries, and strawberries. I get my organic fruits and vegetables in minutes by walking out my front door. Fresh fruits and vegetables out of your garden taste so much richer than those sold in stores. Also, you will reap great satisfaction when you eat something you grew yourself. If you do not have space for a garden, you might try a container garden where vegetables can grow in pots on a deck or smaller patio space. Last, with the right soil and sufficient light and moisture, you can have a small container garden indoors.

Consider purchasing fresh fruits, vegetables, eggs, meat, and cheese at your local farmer's market. Local growers bring farm to table for many months of the year and provide delicious and nutritious organically grown food. Plus, you will be helping a local small business owner. Many of these local producers also offer Community Supported Agriculture (CSA) or crop sharing where producers connect with consumers who subscribe to a certain amount of the harvest each week of the growing season. Additionally, they can purchase a certain amount of meat, eggs, milk, and cheese products on a regular basis throughout the year. Be sure to confirm with the farmers that they are using organic farming practices without pesticides.

If you can afford organic, go for it. If you are on a limited budget, make it a priority to include fresh fruits and vegetables for you and your family. If you purchase non-organic berries, I have found that soaking berries in vinegar and water helps remove some of the pesticide residue. I use one cup of white vinegar in a large mixing bowl and then fill it with water. I soak the berries for 20 minutes and then rinse them.

Find A Food Plan

To maintain a healthy weight long-term, you will have to find a food plan that works for you. Extreme or crash diet plans can be detrimental to your health and rarely work for the long-term.[65]

Balance is the key; fad diets do not work. Intermittent fasting has recently become popular and strong evidence exists that fasting throughout the month can have wonderful health benefits[66]. When I hear that someone has lost extreme amounts of weight quickly by restricting caloric intake, getting weight loss surgery, or going on an extreme diet plan, I wonder how long they will be able to maintain the weight loss.

I have acquaintances who have had weight loss surgery or severely restricted caloric intake and lost large amounts of weight quickly. It is my belief that they did not learn was what initially caused their weight gain and then how to establish healthier eating patterns. I have observed that within a year of losing the weight, they gained most of it back because they failed to address the root causes of their initial weight gain.

Obesity presents a major challenge. It is more than balancing calorie intake and increasing exercise to burn calories. Most people who are overweight and obese need to deal with the emotional reasons why they overeat or choose not to eat healthy.[67]

Hormones and Weight

Women who are in perimenopause, menopause, or post menopause may have more challenges balancing hormonal changes, diet, and exercise. A variety of hormone imbalances can cause weight gain in middle age. As estrogen levels drop, women might gain increased belly fat and tire more easily.[68] The simultaneous drop in estrogen and rise in cortisol and insulin can cause the body to store excess belly fat. Remember that cortisol is our stress hormone. If women in perimenopause, menopause, or post menopause experience elevated stress levels in addition to increased cortisol, they are more likely to gain weight.

Cortisol levels run higher first thing in the morning for these women. So, it is important to exercise early and eat optimal foods at the right time to reduce cortisol and balance other hormone levels. If you struggle with menopausal symptoms including weight gain, I recommend Debra

Atkinson's *Flipping Fifty* program. Debra is a fitness expert who works with women in the middle and upper age groups. She helps women determine and achieve their health and fitness goals during the latter half of their lives. She has written several books and articles on this topic and is an avid YouTuber and podcaster. Check out her website: www.flippingfifty.com

Food Insecurity and Lack of Healthy Food Choices

Food insecurity is also another problem in the United States. It can be described as a lack of access to a sufficient supply of food particularly healthy food choices. This inadequate access may be due to consumers without financial resources or because neighborhoods lack grocery stores that sell healthy food choices. We also have a large number of people who are food insecure in this country. This number grew as the economy took a downturn during the COVID. According to the USDA[69], 10.5 percent of American households are food insecure. That is only slightly lower than the 12.9 percent of the world's population that does not have enough food to lead a healthy, active lifestyle as reported on the Food Aid Foundation's website[70]. These numbers may increase in the years after the pandemic because more people in America might need to rely on economic assistance.

A more frightening statistic shows that only one in ten adults in the United States eats the recommended number of daily fruits and vegetables. According to a 2017 Centers for Disease Control report[71], we lack important fruits and vegetables in our diets. Although this report included only adults, I suspect that the number of children consuming enough fruits and vegetables is even lower. This is based on my observations over the years of how many fruits and vegetables are uneaten and thrown out during school lunch.

It's worth noting that people in poverty are less likely to consume fruits and vegetables. This may be due to several factors. Produce costs more than many other unhealthy choices in the grocery aisle. Some people, particularly in urban areas, live in "food deserts" which means they are not near a store with a good selection of produce.[72]

"Food deserts" can also be found in the thousands of small rural communities across in America that house people with lower incomes or seniors who no longer can drive. Many of these small towns have lost local grocery stores that carry fresh fruits and vegetables. "Low Dollar" stores with very few healthy choices have replaced local stores and offer mostly high fat, high sodium, canned, or processed low-cost foods. Many residents have no choice but to purchase their groceries from these "Low Dollar" stores. When I lived in small-town Iowa, we had a small grocery store, but that store has since closed. The closest town that had a store with a decent selection of healthy foods was 10 miles away. I was fortunate and had a reliable vehicle to drive the distance for shopping, but some families have limited access to grocery stores with healthy food choices.

Convenience stores are popular both in urban and small rural areas and offer few, if any, healthy food choices. In these stores, food costs more, and the convenience makes it easy to choose less healthy food. A pizza, hot dogs or fried chicken and a liter of soda pop from one of these stores make for quick and easy meals for busy families. Yet, these sorts of convenience store meals offer little nutritional value.

Cheap, fast-food also draws families on limited incomes or those who want convenience. A kids' meal is just a few dollars and can be served up in minutes. Yet, traditionally, these meals offer few healthy ingredients. In a positive trend in recent years, more fast-food restaurants now offer customers healthier sides and drinks rather than fries and soda pop at little or no additional charge. Many of these same restaurants offer delicious main dish salads which can make fast-food healthier. Kudos to these fast-food chain restaurants, but people still must make the choice to eat these healthier alternatives.

The Role of Food on Your Immune System

A healthy diet also boosts your immune system. Many foods, herbs, and supplements can enhance your immune system. During COVID-19, and in any given flu season, I think we should jump at the chance to keep our immunity at peak levels to fight viruses. It is surprising that few health experts discuss the immune-boosting power of certain foods, herbs, and supplements to fight off illness. It is my belief that most everyone could benefit from consuming immune-boosting foods along with drinking plenty of water, exercising and reducing stress to help prevent illness. There are no cure-all foods, but the following foods and supplements have boosted my immune system and kept me healthy. I am sure there are more that I have yet to discover and will keep adding them as I continue my wellness journey.

Immune Boosting Foods and Seeds:

1. Almonds & walnuts
2. Blueberries
3. Citrus fruits
4. Cruciferous vegetables such as broccoli, Brussels sprouts, cabbage, cauliflower, kale and radishes
5. Garlic
6. Ginger
7. Onions
8. Green leafy vegetables such as arugula, salad greens, spinach
9. Raw unfiltered honey (caution: This should not be fed to children under age one as it may cause botulism poisoning)
10. Red bell peppers
11. Seeds such as flax and chia

12. Yogurt and other probiotic foods to promote gut health

Immune Boosting Supplements:
13. Magnesium
14. Turmeric
15. Vitamin C
16. Zinc

You should always check with your medical doctor and/or dietician before making any additions or changes to your diet. This is especially true if you have a medical condition that may be affected by the consumption of any of my suggestions. I am not a medical doctor or licensed dietician and only give this advice out of my own experiences and research.

If you are working on improving your wellness with healthy nutrition, I advise you to start with a healthy eating plan. You may want to make an appointment with a registered dietician to assist you in developing a healthy eating plan. If you do nothing, nothing will change.

Can you commit to eating five fruits or vegetables every day? Sneak them in throughout the day. It is not difficult. I admit it takes more time to prepare a leafy green salad than to grab a quick microwave meal or sugary snack. It is a change in mindset that can create new habits. You might have to take time the night before to prepare the following day's lunch to keep yourself from grabbing a quick unhealthy lunch.

It might help if you make your kitchen a place to prepare healthy foods, while you connect with family and/or friends. When you cook together, it might reduce stress and give everyone an opportunity to contribute to staying on a healthy eating regimen. This might be especially beneficial for children in your family. They might be more inclined to make healthy food choices when they help prepare the food and understand its nutritional benefits.

Last, it helps me to think about food as medicine. Will the food that you are putting in your mouth bring your body healing and wellness or tear it down toward illness? When I was diagnosed with Celiac, I changed my mindset about eating gluten. I think this idea might also be helpful to others who struggle with eating unhealthy foods. When I see a delicious-looking food that is wheat-based with gluten, I say to myself, "Poison, poison, that food is poison to me." I visualize skull and crossbones across the foods that I should not eat. You might try similar self-talk and visualizations before you choose a food that is a struggle for you.

You can steer your boat to healthier waters when you prioritize your health and take time to plan and prepare fresh and healthy foods. Eating well to improve and maintain a healthy lifestyle is one of the best ways you control how you look and feel. Just start somewhere! Control your food intake and don't let food control you to the depths of the sea. Set sail for good nutrition and see how far you go on your nutrition journey. You will have food diversions and those icebergs that try and capsize you but stay the course to good nutrition.

Action Steps for Nutrition:

1. Drink plenty of water. Many times, when you think you are hungry, you are likely dehydrated. Plus, water fills your stomach and boosts immunity.

2. Plan out healthy home-cooked meals with others in your household. Try to purchase only grocery items that are in the meal plan and will not tempt you. Reduce the amount of processed, pre-packaged meals as these are often loaded with high amounts of fat, sugar, sodium, carbs, and preservatives.

3. Prepare or purchase healthy snacks that you can choose when the temptation arises to grab an unhealthy snack. Here are some of my go-to snacks:

fruit, healthy popcorn, veggie or sweet potato chips, healthy granola bars, yogurt, or fruit popsicles. A small piece of dark chocolate may help with those chocolate cravings.

4. Be mindful when you eat. Pay attention to the food you ingest and whether you are eating because you are hungry or because you are stressed or emotional. This is a big challenge for me as too often I eat in front of the TV and don't pay attention to my food intake.

5. If you are tempted to eat unhealthy or snack too often, take a walk, go for a bike ride, listen to or play music or dance to de-stress.

The RMS Titanic sinking with passengers in lifeboats.

10

STOP LISTENING TO THE MUSIC AND FIND THE LIFEBOATS

On April 14, 1912, the RMS Titanic sunk in the early morning hours in the North Atlantic Ocean. The ship carried 2,200 passengers and crew and left Southampton, England on its maiden voyage to New York City. It was thought to be unsinkable. It measured one sixth of a mile long, 75 feet high and had hundreds of portholes and four enormous funnels. The ship had many luxuries which were prioritized over lifeboats and other safety features. The crew's radio operators were warned several times of iceberg fields in the area but did not heed those warnings.

The ship struck the icebergs which caused catastrophic damage. As the boat filled with water, most passengers remained unaware of the danger below them. In fact, passengers received no warnings. Lawrence Beesley, a survivor, wrote the book, *The Loss of the SS Titanic*.[73] He stated, "The great majority of passengers were never enlightened as to the amount of damage done, or even as to what had happened." He further wrote that many passengers were told that the ship could not sink for two to three days. So, they remained on deck rather than getting in a lifeboat. As a result, many lifeboats were lowered only partially filled while many people remained on deck where an eight-piece band played music to calm passengers. The ship went down in a matter of hours rather than days. No other rescue ships were close enough to save the large number of crew and passengers. Of the 2,220 passengers aboard ship, 700 people survived. Those that perished went down with the ship or attempted to swim to the lifeboats and died of hypothermia.

What is the lesson here? You cannot wait on deck and listen to music while the boat sinks, and the lifeboats leave the ship. When you are sinking, you must do something drastic. Maybe you feel like you have been seeing some icebergs ahead. Perhaps, you've been bailing water or watching your ship sink for a long time. Are you are wondering when the lifeboats are coming and how you can be rescued?

Put on Your Life Jacket

Is your life jacket secured? What are your next steps in keeping your head above water? What is one thing you can do today to reduce stress and/or improve your wellbeing? What will help you get on your wellness boat? The L.E.A.R.N. principles outlined in this book can be your guide to reduce stress and improve your wellness.

Laugh every day!
Exercise on a regular basis!
Develop an **Attitude** of Gratitude!
Take time to **Relax, Reflect, and Recharge!**
Make some changes to your **Nutrition!**

Have you ever gone sailing, boating, or kayaking on a calm lake or been on a cruise ship when the water is calm? It seems so peaceful and relaxing. That calm might tempt you not to put on your life jacket. But that safety flotation device can save you should you go overboard. Sure, you would get wet, stressed, and bruised up, but you would probably survive. Your head would stay above water, and eventually you would get back into the boat. So, put on your lifejacket with the L.E.A.R.N ideas, get out of the stressful waters, and get in your wellness boat.

As I conclude this book, here are some last thoughts on keeping your head above water. Nearly 70 percent of the Earth and 60 percent of our bodies are made up of water. We need water to survive and thrive physically. But as much as we need to drink fresh, clean water, we can also be swept away by a raging river, flood, or storm surge. On another day, water can calm us as we sit by a peaceful lake. Water changes the landscape. You change as you choose a healthy lifestyle in your wellness boat. The alternative might mean you sink that wellness boat.

In the movie, *The Dead Poets Society,* Robin Williams' character, Mr. Keating, said, "Seize the day. Make your lives extraordinary."[74] Mr. Keating was an English teacher who challenged his students to live the life they were meant to live. What healthy lifestyle habits could you change and implement that can help you live an extraordinary life? Where can you reduce stress and find more peace and joy? Take the opportunities you have today and seize the day!

H. Jackson Brown Jr. from his book, *P.S. I love you*, put it this way, "Twenty years from now you will be more disappointed by the things that you didn't do than by the ones you did do. So, throw off the bow lines. Sail away from the safe harbor. Catch the trade winds in your sails. Explore. Dream. Discover."[75]

Keeping your head above water takes work and dedication. When you feel the sharks pulling you under, stay the course. You must start somewhere on your wellness journey. Find one principle to help you begin and gradually add more. This slow and steady pace will keep you from being overwhelmed by implementing all five of them at once.

You are worth it! You can do this! You were put on this Earth for a purpose and to live your best life. You are the captain of your wellness ship, and it is not too late to set sail in the right direction. When you apply the L.E.A.R.N principles outlined in this book, you will explore, dream and discover more peace, better health, and throw stress overboard!

Find your "why" toward your health behavior change. What will ultimately help you reduce your stress level and improve your wellness? YOU! Only you can make the changes you wish to see in your life. Set goals and take it one day at a time. You might take one step forward and two steps back, but you will move forward. With these principles, you will find wellness and live a healthy, active, and joyful life in a stress-filled world!

Endnotes

Chapter 1
[1] (American Psychological Association)
[2] (Czeisler, 2020)
[3] (Rath, 2004)
[4] (Gallup, 2014)

Chapter 2
[5] (Tan, 2018)
[6] (Institute of Mental Health, n.d.)
[7] (Palmer, 2007)
[8] (Cannon, 1915)
[9] (Cohen, 1983)
[10] (Kermott, 2019)
[11] (Hildenbrand, 2010)

Chapter 3
[12] (Martin R. , 2002)
[13] (Rath, 2004)
[14] (Romero, 2008)
[15] (Cousins, 1979)
[16] (Cousins, 1979)
[17] (Adams, 1998)
[18] (Martin R. , 2002)

Chapter 4
[19] (Franzini, 2002)
[20] (Brown S. , 2009)
[21] (Robinson, 2016)
[22] (Connell, 2014)

Chapter 5
[23] (Centers For Disease Control)

[24] (Centers for Disease Control, 2016)
[25] (Ward, 2019)
[26] (Modoldt, 2008)
[27] (Lee, 2014)
[28] (Medina, 2008)
[29] (Ratey, 2008)
[30] (Gage, 1999)
[31] (Ratey, 2008)
[32] (Hillman, 2009)

Chapter 6
[33] (Simmons, 2015)
[34] (American Customer Satisfaction Index Restaurant Report 2019-2020, 2020)
[35] (Pruyser, 1976)
[36] (Lambert, 2009)
[37] (World Happiness Report, 2020)
[38] (World Economic Forum, 2019)
[39] (World Happiness Report, 2020; Twenge J. , 2019)
[40] (Shevenock, 2020)
[41] (Twenge J. M., 2015)
[42] (Johnson, 2019)
[43] (Einolf, 2011)

Chapter 7
[44] (Bureau of Labor Statistics, 2016)
[45] (Rogers, 2003)
[46] (Westlake)
[47] (The Fred Rogers Company, 2001)

Chapter 8
[48] (Charlie Rose, 1994)
[49] (Pellicane, 2021)
[50] (American Council on Exercise, 2019)
[51] (Beccuti, 2011)
[52] (Kahatsu, 2006)
[53] (American Council on Exercise, 2019)
[54] (Sleep Foundation, 2021)

[55] (Centers for Disease Control, 2014)
[56] (American Council on Exercise, 2019)
[57] (Coleman, 2012)
Chapter 9
[58] (Myers., 2015)
[59] (Merriam-Webster, n.d.)
[60] (Shiel, n.d.)
[61] (Martin C. H., 2018)
[62] (Myers., 2015)
[63] (Hung, 2004)
[64] (Ornish, 2019)
[65] (Jacques, 2014)
[66] (Patterson, 2017)
[67] (Chesler, 2012)
[68] (Atkinson 2016)
[69] (Unitied States Department of Agriculture:Economic Research
Service, 2019)
[70] (Food Aid Foundation, 2019)
[71] (Lee-Kwan, 2017)
[72] (United States Department of Agriculture Economic Research
Service, 2009)

Chapter 10
[73] (Beesely, 1912)
[74] (Weir, 1989)
[75] (Brown H. J., 1990)

Works Cited

Adams, P. (1998). *House Calls.* San Francisco: Robert D. Reed.

American Council on Exercise. (2019). *The Professional's guide to Health and Wellness Coaching.* San Diego, California: Amercian Council on Exercise.

American Customer Satisfaction Index Restaurant Report 2019-2020. (2020). *American Customer Satisfaction.* Michigan: American Customer Satisfaction Index. Retrieved February 19 2021, from https://www.theacsi.org/news-and-resources/customer-satisfaction-reports/reports-2020/acsi-restaurant-report-2019-2020

American Psychological Association. (n.d.). *Stress in America.* Retrieved November 11, 2020, from American Psychological Association: https://www.apa.org/news/press/releases/stress/2015/snapshot

Atkinson, D. (2016). *You Sill Got It, Girl: The After 50 Fitness Formula for Women.* Montery, California: Healthy Learning.

Beccuti, G. P. (2011, July). Sleep and Obesity. *Clinical Nutrition and Metabolic Care, 14*(4), 402-412. Retrieved November 20, 2020, from https://journals.lww.com/co-clinicalnutrition/Abstract/2011/07000/Sleep_and_obesity.16.aspx

Beesely, L. (1912). *The Loss of the SS Titanic.* Boston and New York: Houghton Mifflin Company. Retrieved from https://www.google.com/books/edition/The_Loss_of_t he_SS_Titanic/cRV0ocna7OIC?hl=en&gbpv=1&printsec= frontcover

Brown, H. J. (1990). *P. S. I Love You: When Mom Wrote, She Always Saved the Best for Last.* Nashville, TN: Rutledge Hill Press.

Brown, S. (2009). *Play: How It Shapes the Brain, Opens the Imagination, and Invorates the Soul.* New York, NY: Penguin Books LtD.

Bureau of Labor Statistics. (2016, February 25). *News Release.* Retrieved January 20, 2020, from Bureau of Labor Statistics: https://www.bls.gov/news.release/pdf/volun.pdf

Cannon, W. (1915). *Bodily Changes in Pain, Hunger, Fear and Rage.* New York, NY: D. Appleton & Company.

Centers for Disease Control. (2005, September 23). *Morbidity and Mortality Weekly Report.* Retrieved February 6, 2020, from https://www.cdc.gov/mmwr/preview/mmwrhtml/mm5 437a7.htm

Centers For Disease Control. (n.d.). *2008-2018 Physical Activity Guidelines.* Retrieved December 13, 2019, from CDC.gov: https://www.cdc.gov/physicalactivity/downloads/trend s-in-the-prevalence-of-physical-activity-508.pdf

Centers for Disease Control. (2014). *Sleep and Sleep Disorders*. Retrieved February 20, 2020, from https://www.cdc.gov/sleep/data_statistics.html

Centers for Disease Control. (2016). *CDC.gov*. Retrieved December 12, 2019, from Prevalence of Obesity Among Adults and Youth: United States, 2015-2016: https://www.cdc.gov/nchs/data/databriefs/db288.pdf

Charlie Rose. (1994, September 20). *The Power of Questions*. Retrieved February 6, 2020, from https://charlierose.com/videos/5544

Chesler, B. (2012). Emotional Eating: A Virtually Untreated Risk Factor for Outcome Following Bariatric Surgery. *Scientific World Journal, 2012*. Retrieved April 17, 2021, from https://www.hindawi.com/journals/tswj/2012/365961/

Cohen, S. K. (1983). A Global Measure of Perceived Stress. *Journal of Health and Social Behavior*, 385-396.

Coleman, J. C. (2012, December 6). *https://hbr.org*. Retrieved April 16, 2021, from Harvard Business Review Work-Life Balance: https://hbr.org/2012/12/the-upside-of-downtime

Connell, G. M. (2014). *A Moving Child is a Learning Child: How the Body Teaches the Brain to Think*. Minneapolis, MN: Free Spirit Publishing.

Cousins, N. (1979). *Anatomy of an Illiness Perceived by the Patient: Reflections on Healing and Regeneration*. New York, NY: W.W. Norton & Company, Inc.

Czeisler, M. L.-C. (2020, August 14). *Centers for Disease Control.* Retrieved October 21, 2020, from https://www.cdc.gov/mmwr/volumes/69/wr/mm6932a 1.htm

Einolf, C. (2011, April 6). The Link Between Religion and Helping Others: The Roll of Values, Ideas, and Language. *Sociology of Religion, 72*(4), pp. 435-455. Retrieved April 15, 2021, from https://academic.oup.com/socrel/article-abstract/72/4/435/1612692?redirectedFrom=fulltext

Food Aid Foundation. (2019). *Hunger Statistics.* Retrieved February 26, 2020, from https://www.foodaidfoundation.org/about-hunger.html

Franzini, L. (2002). *Kids Who Laugh: How to Develop Your Child's Sense of Humor: Instilling the Gift of Laughter as a Lifetime Tool for Success.* Garden City Park, NY: Square One Publishers.

Gage, F. V. (1999). Running Increases Cell Proliferation and Neurogenesis in the Adult Mouse Dentate Gyrus. *Nature America Inc*, 266-270. Retrieved December 19, 2019, from http://neurogenesisresearch.com/Runing_and_Neurog enesis_Nat.pdf

Gallup. (2014). *State of America's Schools: The Path to Winning Again in Education.* Omaha: Gallup Inc. Retrieved December 2, 2020, from https://www.gallup.com/education/269648/state-america-schools-report.aspx

Hildenbrand, L. (2010). *Unbroken: A World War II Story of*

Survival, Resilience, and Redemption. New York, NY: Random House.

Hillman, C. P. (2009). The Effect of Acute Treadmill Walking on Cognitive Control and Academic Achievement in Preadolescent Children. *Neuroscience*, 1044-1054. Retrieved December 19, 2019, from https://www.ncbi.nlm.nih.gov/pmc/articles/PMC26678 07/

Hung, H. J.-W. (2004, November). Fruit and Vegetable Intake and Risk of Major Chronic Disease. *Journal of the National Cancert Institute, 96*(21), 1577-1584. Retrieved February 26, 2020, from tps://academic.oup.com/jnci/article/96/21/1577/25210 33

Institute of Mental Health. (n.d.). *5 Things You Should Know About Stress*. Retrieved November 11, 2020, from https://www.nimh.nih.gov/health/publications/stress/i ndex.shtml#pub1

Jacques, J. (2014, Fall). *Obesity Action Coalition*. Retrieved April 17, 2021, from https://www.obesityaction.org/community/article-library/the-risks-of-the-crash-diet/

Johnson, J. (2019, April 18). *Gallup Politics.* Retrieved 18 2020, January, from Gallup: https://news.gallup.com/poll/248837/church-membership-down-sharply-past-two-decades.aspx

Kahatsu, N. T. (2006, September 18). Sleep Duration and Body

Mass Index in Rural Population. *Journal of American Medical Association, 166*(16), 17-1-1705. Retrieved February 6, 2020, from https://jamanetwork.com/article.aspx?doi=10.1001/archinte.166.16.1701

Kermott, C. J. (2019). *Is higher resilience predictive of lower stress and better mental health among corporate executives?* Retrieved October 25, 2020, from https://journals.plos.org/plosone/article?id=10.1371/journal.pone.0218092#sec012

Lambert, N. F. (2009). More gratitude, less materialism: The mediating role of life satisfaction. *The Journal of Positive Pschology*, 32-42. Retrieved November 18, 2020, from https://www.tandfonline.com/doi/abs/10.1080/17439760802216311

Lee, D. (2014, July). Leisure-Time Running Reduces All-Cause and Cardiovascular Mortality Risk. *Journal of the American College of Cardiology, 64*(5), 472-481. Retrieved December 18, 2019, from https://www.jacc.org/doi/full/10.1016/j.jacc.2014.04.058

Lee-Kwan, S. M. (2017, November 17). *Disparities in State-Specific Adult Fruit and Vegetable Consumption.* United States: Centers for Disease Control: Morbidity and Mortality Weekly Report. Retrieved February 26, 2020, from Disparities in State-Specific Adult Fruit and Vegetable Consumption-United States 2015: https://www.cdc.gov/mmwr/volumes/66/wr/mm6645a1.htm?s_cid=mm6645a1_w

Martin, C. H. (2018, July). *Attempts to Lose Weight Among Adults in the United States 2013-2016.* Retrieved February 26, 2020, from Centers for Disease Control: https://www.cdc.gov/nchs/data/databriefs/db313.pdf

Martin, R. (2002, December). Is Laughter the Best Medicine? Humor, Laughter, and Physical Health. *Current Directions in Psychological Science*, 216-220.

Medina, J. (2008). *Brain Rules: 12 Principles for Surviving and Thriving at Work, Home, and School.* Seattle, WA: Pear Press.

Merriam-Webster. (n.d.). *Merium-Webster.* Retrieved February 20, 2020, from https://www.merriam-webster.com/dictionary/nourish

Modoldt, T. W. (2008, December 1). Physical activity and mortality in men and women with coronary heart disease: a prospective population-based cohort study in Norway (the HUNT study). *European Journal of Preventative Cardiology, Volume: 15* (6), 639-645. Retrieved from https://journals.sagepub.com/doi/full/10.1097/HJR.0b013e3283101671

Myers., A. (2015). *The Autoimmune Solution: Prevent and Reverse the Full Spectrum of Inflammatory Symptoms and Diseases.* New York: Harper One.

Ornish, D. (2019). *UnDo It! How Simple Lifestyle Changes Can Reverse Most Chronic Diseases.* New York, NY: Ballatine Books.

Palmer, S. C. (2007). *How to Deal with Stress: Creating Success.*

London, England: Kogan Page Limited.

Patterson, R. S. (2017). Metabolic Effects of Intermittent Fasting. *Annual Review of Nutrition*, 371-385.

Pellicane, A. (2021, March 22). *What Are You Picking Up*. Retrieved March 22, 2021, from https://proverbs31.org/read/devotions/full-post/2021/03/22/what-are-you-picking-up

Pruyser, P. (1976). *The Minister as Diagnostician: Personal Problems in Pastoral Perspective.* Philadelphia, PA: PA: Westminster Press.

Ratey, J. (2008). *Spark: The Revolutionary New Science of Exercise and the Brain.* New York, NY: Little Brown and Company.

Rath, T. C. (2004). *How Full Is Your Bucket.* New York: Gallup Press.

Robinson, K. A. (2016). *Creative Schools: The Grassroots Revolution That's Transforming Education.* New York, NY: Penguin Random House LLC.

Rogers, F. (2003). *The World According to Mister Rogers, Important Things to Remember.* New York, NY: Hachette Books.

Romero, E. P. (2008). Humor and Group Effectiveness. *Human Relations*, 407.

Shevenock, S. (2020, August 20). *Education and Entertainment.* Retrieved April 15, 2021, from https://morningconsult.com: https://morningconsult.com/2020/08/20/youtube-netflix-and-gaming-a-look-at-what-kids-are-doing-with-their-increased-screen-time/

Shiel, W. (n.d.). *MedicineNet: Medical Definition of Nutrition.* Retrieved February 26, 2020, from https://www.medicinenet.com/nutrition/definition.htm

Simmons, K. (2015, December 12). *Good Teachers Don't Quit: 5 Ways to Avoid Teacher Burnout.* Retrieved January 16, 2020, from YouTube: https://www.youtube.com/watch?v=Ap_LKQzVeR8

Sleep Foundation. (2021, January 8). *The LInk Between Sleep and Job Performance.* Retrieved April 16, 2021, from https://www.sleepfoundation.org: https://www.sleepfoundation.org/sleep-hygiene/good-sleep-and-job-performance

Tan, S. Y. (2018, April). Hans Selye: Founder of the Stress Theory. *Singapore Medical Journal*, 170-171.

The Fred Rogers Company. (2001). *Mister Rogers Neighborhorhood.* Retrieved October 22, 2020, from https://misterrogers.org/videos/look-for-the-helpers/

Twenge, J. (2019). *The Sad State of Happiness in the United States and the Role of Digital Media.* New York: Sustainable Development Solutions Network,. Retrieved 18 2020, January, from https://worldhappiness.report/ed/2019/the-sad-state-of-happiness-in-the-united-states-and-the-role-of-digital-media/

Twenge, J. M. (2015, May 11). Generational and Time Period Differences in American Adolescents' Religious

Orientation: 1966-2014. *PLOS One, 14*(8), 1-17.
Retrieved January 18, 2020, from
https://journals.plos.org/plosone/article?id=10.1371/jo
urnal.pone.0221441

United States Department of Agriculture Economic Research
Service. (2009). *Access to Affordable and Nutritious
Food: Measuring and Understanding Food Deserts and
Their Consequences.* United States Department of
Agriculture. Retrieved April 18, 2021, from
https://www.ers.usda.gov/webdocs/publications/42711
/12716_ap036_1_.pdf?v=6119.2

Unitied States Department of Agriculture:Economic Research
Service. (2019). *Food Security and Nutrition Assistance.*
Retrieved November 20, 2020, from
https://www.ers.usda.gov/data-products/ag-and-food-
statistics-charting-the-essentials/food-security-and-
nutrition-assistance/

Ward, Z. B. (2019, December). Projected U.S. State-Level
Prevalence of Adult Obesity and Severe Obesity. *New
England Journal of Medicine*, 2440-2450. Retrieved
December 2019, from
https://www.nejm.org/doi/full/10.1056/NEJMsa190930
1

Weir, P. (Director). (1989). *The Dead Poet's Society* [Motion
Picture]. Retrieved November 20, 2020, from
https://www.youtube.com/watch?v=vi0Lbjs5ECI

Westlake, C. (n.d.). *Why Letting Others Help You is a Gift.*
Retrieved January 29, 2020, from Live a Different
Beautiful: Courtney Westlake:

https://www.courtneywestlake.com/why-letting-others-help-you-is-a-gift

World Economic Forum. (2019, March 21). *Finland is the happiest country-again.* Retrieved November 18, 2020, from https://www.weforum.org/agenda/2019/03/finland-is-the-world-s-happiest-country-again/

World Happiness Report. (2020). *World Happiness Report 2020.* New York: Sustainable Development Solutions Network.

ABOUT THE AUTHOR

Sally Shaver DuBois is an educator, entertainer, professional speaker and author of the new book, *Keeping Your Head Above Water*. A wellness professional, Sally has spent 30+ years helping people of all ages to live a healthy, active lifestyle. As a professional speaker, personal trainer, health and physical educator, and certified health coach, she has guided thousands of people to improve their lives. Additionally, a certified laughter leader, Sally entertains audiences across the Midwest and around the USA. **Silly Sally** performs singing telegrams, balloon creations, original music, ventriloquism, and magic to audiences of all ages because she believes laughter truly is the best medicine!

Sally received her BS in physical education, health and music at Iowa State University. She also has a master's degree in human performance from Minnesota State University and a master's degree in curriculum and instructional technology from Iowa State University. She lives with her husband, Paul and their animals in the country near Ames, Iowa. She enjoys exercising along the country roads, writing, playing and singing music, gardening, training her dogs, and taking photos of the beautiful sunrises and sunsets over the Iowa corn and bean fields.

Learn more about Sally at https://www.dolifewellnow.com/

Made in the USA
Columbia, SC
10 June 2021